GUM

Language Skills 5
Student Guide

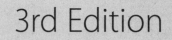
3rd Edition

Illustrations Credits

All illustrations © K12 Inc. unless otherwise noted

About K12 Inc.

K12 Inc., a technology-based education company, is the nation's leading provider of proprietary curriculum and online education programs to students in grades K–12. K¹² provides its curriculum and academic services to online schools, traditional classrooms, blended school programs, and directly to families. K12 Inc. also operates the K¹² International Academy, an accredited, diploma-granting online private school serving students worldwide. K¹²'s mission is to provide any child the curriculum and tools to maximize success in life, regardless of geographic, financial, or demographic circumstances. K12 Inc. is accredited by CITA. More information can be found at www.K12.com.

ISBN: 978-1-60153-468-2

Printed by LSC Communications, Kendallville, IN, USA, April 2017

Table of Contents

Name _____ Date _____

Unit 1 Pretest

Part 1: Periods
Add periods where needed.

1. John H Rollins was born on Jan 1, 1900

2. My mother wakes us up at 7:00 am every morning

3. Catch the bus that goes to Claytor Ave and get off at the last stop

4. On Tues we will tour Washington DC and Arlington

5. Give this letter to Dr Thompkins

Part 2: Commas
Add commas where needed.

6. Boys and girls the playground is closed today.

7. Sometimes Tammy you work too quickly and make careless mistakes.

8. No we do not need a new telephone.

9. Have you finished eating your lunch Seth?

10. The towels Ruth are in the closet.

Unit 1 Pretest

Part 3: Exclamation Points and Question Marks
Add exclamation points and question marks where needed.

11. Were you startled when the door slammed

12. There's a huge fish on my line

13. Who taught you how to play the guitar

14. Look out for those falling rocks

15. When is the train scheduled to arrive

Part 4: Apostrophes
Add apostrophes where needed.

16. Well be disappointed if you arent able to come to dinner at our house.

17. A snakes bite can be dangerous and even deadly.

18. The guide said we shouldnt get too close to the edge of the cliff.

19. Theyll need to borrow Tinas camera for the photography project.

20. This trees leaves dont fall off in the winter.

Name _____   Date _____

Get Ready

Study these guidelines for using commas. Each example has at least one practice item for you to complete or correct. Write your answers on this page.

1. Use a comma to separate words in a series.
A series is a list of items. When you write a list of items in a sentence, separate the items with commas.

    Incorrect: Monday Tuesday and Wednesday are my days to feed the cat.
    Correct: Monday, Tuesday, and Wednesday are my days to feed the cat.

    Practice 1:   The cat eats fish chicken pasta and mouse.

_____

2a. Use a comma after the salutation and complimentary close of a letter.
The salutation is the greeting that begins a letter.

    Incorrect: Dear Jerry
    Correct: Dear Jerry,

    Practice 2a: Dear Madam or Sir

_____

2b. The complimentary close is the sign-off or good-bye at the end of the letter, before the sender's name.

    Incorrect: Your friend.
    Correct: Your friend,

Practice 2b: With best wishes

_____

3a. Use a comma in a date between the day of the month and the year.
When you write the month, day, and year of a date, put a comma before the year.

Incorrect: I was born on July 25 1992.
Correct: I was born on July 25, 1992.

Practice 3a: Danny's birthday is October 7 1990.

_____

3b. When you write the date, put another comma after the year if the date does not end the sentence.

Incorrect: July 15, 1992 is the day I arrived.
Correct: July 15, 1992, is the day I arrived.

Practice 3b: October 7 1990 is when Danny was born.

_____

3c. If you are writing only the month and the year, you don't need a comma.

Incorrect: July, 1992 was a very good month!
Correct: July 1992 was a very good month!

Practice 3c: October, 1990, was happy for Danny's parents.

_____

4a. Use a comma between the name of a city and the state or country.
When you write the name of a place using the city or town name and state or country name, put a comma before the state or country.

Incorrect: Grandpa lives in Richmond Virginia.
Correct: Grandpa lives in Richmond, Virginia.

Practice 4a: Have you visited Paris France?

_____

4b. When you write the name of a place, put another comma after the name of the state or country if it does not end the sentence.

Incorrect: Richmond, Virginia is where Grandpa lives.
Correct: Richmond, Virginia, is where Grandpa lives.

Practice 4b: Paris France is a beautiful city.

_____

Name _____   Date _____

Get Ready

When you quote a speaker's exact words, it is called a direct quotation. A direct quotation can stand alone or be part of another sentence.

Read this piece from the story of Red Riding Hood. The direct quotations are underlined.

"Good morning, Grandmother. Here are some cakes and berries for you," said Red Riding Hood.

"I am so glad," smiled the wolf, "to see you."

The girl said, "Grandmother, what large eyes you have!"

"The better to see your lovely face," answered the wolf.

"Grandmother," exclaimed Red Riding Hood, "what long arms you have!"

"The better," said the creature, "to hug you, sweetie."

"But why are your teeth so sharp, Grandmother?" Red Riding Hood asked.

"So that, my dear," replied the wicked wolf, "I may eat you!"

Later that night, Red Riding Hood told her mother, "I will never talk to a wolf again."

Punctuation for Direct Quotations

1. Whenever you quote a speaker's exact words, surround them with quotation marks.

   "Good morning, Grandmother. Here are some cakes and berries for you," said Red Riding Hood.

   "I am so glad," smiled the wolf, "to see you."

2. Use a comma to end the part of a sentence before a direct quotation.

   The girl said, "Grandmother, what large eyes you have!"

3. Use a comma to end a direct quotation if the rest of the sentence follows the quotation.

   "The better to see your lovely face," answered the wolf.

4. If a direct quotation is split up in a sentence, use commas before and after each part of the quotation to separate it from the rest of the sentence.

   "Grandmother," exclaimed Red Riding Hood, "what long arms you have!"

   "The better," said the creature, "to hug you, sweetie."

5. If you are quoting a question, put the quotation marks outside the question mark.

> "But why are your teeth so sharp, Grandmother?" Red Riding Hood asked.

6. If you are quoting an exclamation, put the quotation marks outside the exclamation point.

> "So that, my dear," replied the wicked wolf, "I may eat you!"

7. If you are quoting a statement, put the quotation marks outside the period.

> Later that night, Red Riding Hood told her mother, "I will never talk to a wolf again."

Name _____   Date _____

Get Ready

Conjunctions

When you want to combine two sentences into one longer sentence, you usually use a special little connector word called a *conjunction*. Three of the most common conjunctions are *and, but,* and *or.*

Combining Two Sentences with a Comma and a Conjunction

A comma is important when you want to join two sentences together. It signals, "Slow down! Read carefully!"

When you want to combine two sentences, you replace the end punctuation of the first sentence with a comma, add a conjunction, and then write the second sentence. For example:

Two sentences: You know what a comma is.
                      What is a conjunction?

Combined sentence: You know what a comma is,but what is a conjunction?

Two sentences: Put a comma at the end of the first sentence.
                      Add a conjunction before the second sentence.

Combined sentence: Put a comma at the end of the first sentence,and add a
                      conjunction before the second sentence.

Two sentences: You can combine related sentences.
                      You can leave them alone.

Combined sentence: You can combine related sentences,or you can leave
                      them alone.

Using *And*, *But*, and *Or*

And, *but*, and *or* are all conjunctions, but they mean different things, and so you use them at different times. These definitions and examples will help you understand when to use which conjunction.

And joins ideas that are **similar** or **equal**.

Example:	Put a comma at the end of the first sentence, <u>and</u> add a conjunction before the second sentence.
Similarity?	both instructions are important for joining sentences

But joins ideas that are **different** or **show a contrast**.

Example:	You know what a comma is, <u>but</u> what is a conjunction?
Difference?	you know one definition, but not the other

Or joins ideas that give a **choice** or **alternative**.

Example:	You can combine related sentences, <u>or</u> you can leave them alone.
Choice?	to combine sentences or to leave them alone

Name _____   Date _____

Try It

Join these pairs of sentences using a comma and a conjunction that makes sense. Write your new sentence on the line.

Example:
    Sleepwalkers don't realize what they are doing.
    They can't remember it later.

<u>Sleepwalkers don't realize what they are doing, and they can't remember it later.</u>

1. We spend nearly a third of our lives sleeping.
    It is not a waste of time.

    _____

2. Henry needs eight hours of sleep.
    Fred needs only six hours.

    _____

3. I might sleep in my bed tonight.
    I might use my sleeping bag instead.

    _____

Name _____   Date _____

Commas with Tag Questions

A comma is used to set off a tag question from the rest of a sentence. A tag question is a short question that comes at the end of a sentence.

You are in my swim class, <u>aren't you?</u>

He's not coming to the basketball game, <u>is he</u>?

Always use a comma between the statement and the tag question.

_____

Add a comma to separate the tag question from the rest of the sentence.

1. This is your house isn't it?

2. You're not going to eat that are you?

3. Jack wrote that poem didn't he?

4. These flowers smell strange don't they?

5. I haven't been to the zoo in a long time have I?

6. Sadie didn't sleep very well last night did she?

7. Write a sentence with a tag question about a delicious dinner.

_____

Name _____ Date _____

Try It

Study the guidelines for using commas. Then in each numbered example, add commas where they are needed.

Use a comma after the salutation and complimentary close of a letter.

1. Dear Mom and Dad

2. Love

Use a comma to separate items in a series.

3. The original thirteen colonies included Connecticut Massachusetts and New Hampshire.

Use commas to set off words in direct address. Direct address means speaking directly to a person.

4. Harry in what year was the Boston Tea Party?

5. The Boston Tea Party Philip was in 1773.

Use a comma between the day of the month and the year. Use another comma after the year if the date does not end the sentence.

6. July 4 1776 is called the United States' birthday.

Use a comma between the name of a city and a state or country. Use another comma after the state or country if the geographical name does not end the sentence.

7. The Second Continental Congress met in Philadelphia Pennsylvania to adopt the Declaration of Independence on July 4 1776.

Use a comma after *yes* and *no* when they introduce sentences.

8. No King George III did not sign the Declaration of Independence.

Use commas to separate direct quotations from the rest of the sentence.

9. The first paragraph of the Declaration of Independence begins "We hold these truths to be self-evident."

10. "Did you know" said Selena "that Thomas Jefferson helped to found the University of Virginia?"

Use a comma before conjunctions that join two sentences.

11. John Trumbull painted all the signers of the Declaration of Independence but he focused on six in particular.

12. We see John Hancock sitting at the front of Trumbull's painting and we see John Adams Roger Sherman Robert Livingston Thomas Jefferson, and Benjamin Franklin standing before him.

Name _____   Date _____

Get Ready

In writing, we treat the titles of creative works, such as books, paintings, songs, or poems in special ways.

Books, Movies, TV Shows, Works of Art

If you are writing them out by hand, you underline titles of books, movies, TV shows, or works of art such as paintings or statues.

Titles written by hand: <u>The Wind in the Willows</u> (book)
<u>The Yearling</u> (movie)
<u>The Flintstones</u> (TV show)
<u>The Starry Night</u> (painting)

If you are using a computer or word processor, italicize the titles of books, movies, or works of art such as paintings or statues.

Titles in print: *The Wind in the Willows* (book)
The Yearling (movie)
The Flintstones (TV show)
The Starry Night (painting)

Stories, Poems, Songs

You always put quotation marks around the titles of stories, poems, and songs, whether you write them out by hand or print them on a computer.

"Snow-White and Rose-Red" (story)
"Buckingham Palace" (poem)
"Oh, Susanna" (song)

Just as with most direct quotations, if you write a sentence that contains a title in quotation marks, put a period or comma *inside* the closing quotation marks. For example:

I can sing "Oh, Susanna," by heart, but I'm still learning "The Star-Spangled Banner."

Name _____   Date _____

Try It

Complete the sentences with a title of your choice. Decide whether you should underline the titles or put quotation marks around them.

1. When I was six, my favorite story was_____.

2. One movie I'd like to see is_____.

3. A good lullaby to fall asleep to is_____.

Name _____ Date _____

Get Ready

Study these examples and guidelines for using capital letters, and then practice using them in Try It and *Exercises in English*.

1. Capitalize the first word of a sentence.

Incorrect: a quokka is a kind of kangaroo.
Correct: A quokka is a kind of kangaroo.

2. Capitalize proper nouns, proper adjectives and their abbreviations.

Proper nouns name particular persons, places, or things. Proper adjectives are adjectives formed from proper nouns. Abbreviations of proper nouns include initials.

Incorrect: Have you ever seen an african elephant?
Correct: Have you ever seen an African elephant?

Incorrect: I think I saw one in st. louis, missouri.
Correct: I think I saw one in St. Louis, Missouri.

3. Capitalize important words in titles of books, stories, plays, and other creative works.

Capitalize the first and last words, as well nouns, pronouns, verbs, adverbs, and adjectives. In general, the little words such as the articles, conjunctions, and prepositions are not capitalized.

Incorrect: I will recite the poem "the fairies have never a penny to spend."
Correct: I will recite the poem "The Fairies Have Never a Penny to Spend."

4. Capitalize the first word of a direct quotation.

When we quote someone's exact words, it is called a direct quotation. Direct quotations start with a capital letter.

Incorrect: Marc Antony proclaimed, "friends, Romans, countrymen, lend me your ears."

Correct: Marc Antony proclaimed, "Friends, Romans, countrymen, lend me your ears."

5. Capitalize the first word of each line of poetry.

Capitalize the first letter of the first word of a line of poetry, whether or not it starts a new sentence.

Incorrect: two roads diverged in a wood, and I—
I took the one less traveled by,
and that has made all the difference.

Correct: Two roads diverged in a wood, and I—
I took the one less traveled by,
And that has made all the difference.

6. Capitalize names of deities, the Bible, and other sacred books.

A deity is a divine being: a god or goddess. Sacred books are the holy writings of a religion.

Examples:
Athena, ancient Greek goddess of wisdom
the Koran, the sacred book of Islam

7. Capitalize *north*, *south*, *east*, and *west* when they refer to specific regions of a country.

That is, capitalize *north*, *south*, *east*, and *west* if they are used as proper nouns or adjectives, referring to a specific region of a country. Do not capitalize them if they simply show general direction.

General direction: The sun rises in the east and sets in the west.

Specific region of the country: Mr. Rubinsky was born on the East Coast, but he lives in the Pacific Northwest.

8. Capitalize the first word in the salutation and the complimentary close of a letter, and the name of the person addressed.

The salutation is the greeting that begins a letter, and the complimentary close is the sign-off or good-bye at the end of the letter, before the sender's name.

Incorrect salutation:	To Whom It May Concern,
Correct salutation:	To whom it may concern,
Incorrect complimentary close:	with all good wishes,
Correct complimentary close:	With all good wishes,

9. Capitalize the pronoun *I* and the interjection *O*.

An interjection is a short exclamation that expresses strong feeling or emotion. Examples include *Ow! Aha!* and *Oh no!* You will learn more about interjections in a later lesson.

The interjection *O* is usually used to invoke or address someone. You usually find *O* used in poetry and songs.

Examples: Fanny and I are entering the talent show.
O come, all ye faithful, joyful and triumphant.
O Romeo, Romeo! Wherefore art thou Romeo?

Name _____   Date _____

Try It

Put a ✓ on the line next to each item that is capitalized completely correctly.

_____1. "Home, Home on the range"

_____2. She clapped her hand to her head and said, "oh! I can't believe I
            forgot again!"

_____3. Beaverton Town Hall

_____4. Sincerely yours,

_____5. Go West, young woman!

Name _____   Date _____

Try It

Pretend that you are the teacher correcting a student's paper, below. Circle the student's punctuation or capitalization errors, and fix what is wrong in the space below each item. Not every item has an error.

Example: Get over here right this minute.

minute! _____

1. My favorite poem is <u>Animal Crackers</u>, by Christopher Morley.

   _____

2. Anne Nancy Terrell's initials—ant—make a word.

   _____

3. "Let's go," said the counselor, to the brook.

   _____

4. Today's date is September 30 2003.

   _____

5. My father used to be a truck driver but now he is a salesman.

   _____

6. No, Sally, we don't want to eat worms, bugs, and snakes.

_____

7. My aunt and I are going to Charlotte North Carolina for a trip.

_____

8. You can have soup for lunch or you can have a sandwich.

_____

9. Mom said, has anyone seen my keys?

_____

10. That mockingbird's song is lovely, but the geese's honking is not.

_____

Name _____ Date _____

Unit 2 Pretest

Part 1: Identifying and Classifying Nouns
Underline the noun in each sentence. Does it name a person, place, or a thing? Fill in the bubble.

1. I think I see the mailman outside.
   - ⓐ person
   - ⓑ place
   - ⓒ thing

2. Did the clock break when you dropped it?
   - ⓐ person
   - ⓑ place
   - ⓒ thing

3. They're looking forward to moving to California.
   - ⓐ person
   - ⓑ place
   - ⓒ thing

4. We searched and found several large shells.
   - ⓐ person
   - ⓑ place
   - ⓒ thing

5. Samantha is very courteous and friendly.
   - ⓐ person
   - ⓑ place
   - ⓒ thing

Unit 2 Pretest

Part 2: Proper and Common Nouns
Underline each proper noun and circle each common noun.

6.   Our new car was made at a factory in Japan.

7.   Tourists often visit Holland to see the beautiful tulips.

8.   Jamal read a book about Walt Disney and his imagination.

9.   My uncle is known for the muffins and bagels he makes at his bakery in
     Chicago.

10. Abraham Lincoln declared Thanksgiving to be the fourth Thursday
     in November.

Part 3: Singular and Plural Nouns
Write S on the line if the noun is singular. Write P on the line if the noun is plural.

11. potatoes   _____

12. walrus   _____

13. engineer   _____

14. newspapers   _____

15. hospital   _____

Unit 2 Pretest

Part 4: Using Nouns in Sentences
Complete these sentences by writing a noun on each line. Use each word once.

markers   lions   thermos   stamp   milk

letter   scissors   Africa   crayons   cloth

16. The zookeeper awaited the arrival of the _____ from _____.

17. Please put a _____ on this _____ and mail it for me.

18. Tommy filled his _____ with cold _____.

19. Should I use _____ or _____ for this poster?

20. You'll need a sharp pair of _____ to cut this thick _____.

Name _____   Date _____

Get Ready

Review

A *noun* names a person, place, thing, or idea.

- A *proper noun* names a particular person, place, thing, or idea. Capitalize proper nouns.

- A *common noun* refers to an example of any person, place, thing, or idea. You do not usually capitalize common nouns.

Relationships Between Common and Proper Nouns

Common nouns and proper nouns can be related to each other. You can probably think of specific proper nouns that fall within the general category of a common noun. For example:

Common Noun Category	Proper Noun Examples
sea	Mediterranean Sea, Caspian Sea, Caribbean Sea
road	Interstate 95, Stafford Avenue, Pacific Coast Highway
book	<u>Swiss Family Robinson</u>, <u>Voyage of the Dawn, Treader</u>
leader	Queen Elizabeth, Julius Caesar, George Washington

Another way to see the relationship between common and proper nouns is to look at specific names, or proper nouns. Then, think about what the proper nouns have in common, and decide what broader common noun category they may belong to. For example:

Proper Noun Examples	Common Noun Category
July, December, February	months
Mt. Rushmore, Mt. Washington, Mt. Rainier	mountains
Mississippi River, Thames River, River Nile	rivers
Islam, Judaism, Christianity	religions

Name _____ Date _____

Try It

A. Fill in the blank with a common noun that names a category for the proper nouns.

1. _____   United, Delta, US Airways, Southwest, American

2. _____   Providence, Orlando, Dallas, Phoenix, Seattle

B. List at least one proper noun that names a specific example of each common noun.

3. month _____

4. college or university _____

Name _____ Date _____

Get Ready

In English we can show ownership, or possession, several ways. One way is to use the word *of:*

The papers <u>of</u> Mary (the papers belong to Mary)
The sound <u>of</u> trumpets (the sound belongs to the trumpets)

Another way is to use a *possessive noun*:

<u>Mary's</u> papers
The <u>trumpets'</u> sound

Singular Possessive Nouns

Singular possessive nouns show that *one* person, place, thing, or idea is the owner. To form the singular possessive, add an apostrophe and the letter *s* to the singular noun.

Fill in the blanks with the possessive form of the singular nouns in the left-hand column.

Singular Noun	Singular Possessive Noun	
Connie	_____	jump rope
sky	_____	color

Some singular nouns end in *s* already. To make those nouns possessive, add an apostrophe and then another *s*.

Fill in the blank with the possessive form of singular nouns in the left-hand column.

Singular Noun	Singular Possessive Noun	
Wes	_____	candy
boss	_____	idea

Plural Possessive Nouns

Plural possessive nouns show that *more than one* person, place, thing, or idea owns the item. To form a plural possessive noun, usually you add an apostrophe to the end of the plural noun.

Fill in the blanks with the possessive form of the plural nouns in the middle column.

Singular Noun	Plural Noun	Plural Possessive Noun	
swingset	swingsets	_____	creaks
fly	flies	_____	buzzing

Some nouns are irregular and have plurals that do not end in -s.

How do you make an irregular plural noun, such as *oxen* or *teeth*, possessive? Just add an apostrophe and *s* to the plural noun.

Fill in the blanks with the possessive form of the plural nouns in the middle column.

Singular Noun	Irregular Plural Noun	Irregular Plural Possessive Noun
man	men	_____ team
mouse	mice	_____ holes

Irregular Plural Possessive or Singular Possessive— How Can You Tell?

The possessive of an irregular plural noun looks a lot like a singular possessive noun because they both end with an apostrophe followed by an *s*.

To avoid confusing them, focus on the main word, to the left of the apostrophe. If that is a plural noun, then the word is a plural possessive. If that is a singular noun, the word is a singular possessive. For example:

Jan's game
(Jan is singular, so Jan's is a singular possessive noun)

women's game
(women is plural, so women's is a plural possessive noun)

Name _____   Date _____

Try It

Some of the following sentences use direct address, and some do not. If a sentence uses direct address, write DA on the line and underline the nouns that name the person or persons spoken to.

Example:
    __DA__ Are you having fun painting that fence, <u>Tom Sawyer</u>?

1. _____ Yes I am, Huck; would you like to join me?

2. _____ Becky can't help because she's at the library.

3. _____ Aunt Polly, may we have something to drink?

4. _____ Aunt Polly brought Tom and Huck some lemonade.

5. _____ "Thank you, ma'am," the boys said.

Name   Date

Get Ready

In direct address, you speak right to someone, often using a noun that *names* the person or people spoken to. For example:

>   <u>Mr. and Mrs. Ferguson</u>, I like your new car.
>   What a great idea, <u>Jenny</u>!

Another way to address directly is by using a noun that *describes* or *identifies* the person or people spoken to. For example:

>   It's time, <u>girls</u>, to go home.
>   Thank you, <u>officer</u>.

As you can see in the examples, commas set off the direct address nouns from the rest of the sentence.

Name _____ Date _____

Get Ready

Sentences are groups of words that express a complete thought. A sentence has a subject and a predicate. The *predicate* of a sentence contains the verb and tells more about the subject: what it is, or what it does.

The *subject* of a sentence contains all the words that tell who or what the sentence is about. Sometimes the subject is called the *complete subject*. To find a subject, ask "Who?" or "What?" before the verb.

The *simple subject* of a sentence is the noun or pronoun in the subject that names the person, place, thing, or idea that the sentence is about.

In this example, the subject is underlined, and the simple subject is underlined twice.

   The thin, delicate <u>wings</u> of the butterfly are very beautiful.

Exercises in English will give you more practice with using nouns as simple subjects.

Then, turn to a different activity in Try It: analyzing sentences.

Name _____   Date _____

Try It

Analyze these three sentences by answering the following questions.

Sentence Analysis Questions
1. Is it a sentence or a fragment?
2. What kind of sentence is it?
3. What is the verb?
4. What is the simple subject?
5. Is there a direct object?
6. Are there any modifiers?
7. What part of speech is each word?

1. Many students enjoy sentence analysis daily.

Sentence or fragment?   _____

Kind of sentence?   _____

Verb?   _____

Simple subject?   _____

Direct object, if any?   _____

Modifiers?   _____

Parts of speech?   Many   _____   sentence _____
                     students _____   analysis _____
                     enjoy   _____   daily   _____

2. Some people prefer math problems occasionally.

Sentence or fragment? _____

Kind of sentence? _____

Verb? _____

Simple subject? _____

Direct object, if any? _____

Modifiers? _____

Parts of speech? Some _____ math _____
people _____ problems _____
prefer _____ occasionally _____

3. Other children like science experiments best.

Sentence or fragment? _____

Kind of sentence? _____

Verb? _____

Simple subject? _____

Direct object, if any? _____

Modifiers? _____

Parts of speech? Other _____ science _____
children _____ experiments _____
like _____ best _____

Name _____   Date _____

Get Ready

Thanks for the Complement?

Let's talk about what a *complement* is. A *complement* fills up, balances, or completes something else. For example, interlocking puzzle pieces, two halves of a locket, or a plug and socket are complements to one another.

A complement is <u>not</u> a compliment, or admiring remark. Don't confuse the two. Complement and compliment are homophones—words that sound the same, but have different meanings.

Subject Complements

A subject complement is a noun, pronoun, or adjective that follows a linking verb and completes the meaning of the verb. The subject complement describes the subject.

Read these pairs of sentences and discuss the questions that follow.

1. Mrs. Jones <u>is</u> a gardener.	4. Mrs. Jones hires a gardener.
2. Allison <u>was</u> the leader.	5. Allison chose the leader.
3. Raymond <u>will be</u> a teacher.	6. Raymond likes the teacher.

1. Do Sentences 1-3 on the left have the same meaning as Sentences 4-6 on the right? Explain.

2. What kinds of verb do Sentences 1-3 have?

3. What kinds of verb do Sentences 4-6 have?

Name _____   Date _____

Try It

Identify the subject, linking verb, and subject complement in each of the following sentences. Write your answers on the blank lines under each sentence.

Example: London is the capital of England.
Subject: London_____
Linking verb: is_____
Subject complement: capital_____

1. My father was a computer engineer for IBM.
   Subject: _____
   Linking verb: _____
   Subject complement: _____

2. Alaska is the northernmost state in this country.
   Subject: _____
   Linking verb: _____
   Subject complement: _____

3. Rice Crunch is the best breakfast cereal.
   Subject: _____
   Linking verb: _____
   Subject complement: _____

4. I will be the president of the United States someday.
   Subject: _____
   Linking verb: _____
   Subject complement: _____

5. These big houses were once single-family homes.
   Subject: _____
   Linking verb: _____
   Subject complement: _____

Name _____   Date _____

Get Ready

What Is a Direct Object?

When a sentence has an action verb, it often has a *direct object* also. A direct object is a noun or pronoun that receives the action of an action verb. To find a direct object in a sentence, ask, "Whom?" or "What?" after the action verb.

Compare these sentences. Which one has a direct object? Underline it.

    1. The squirrel scampered all around the yard.

    2. The squirrel gathered nuts all around the yard.

Look at the following sentences. First, underline the action verb of each sentence. Then put two lines under the word that receives the action of the verb. That word is the direct object.

    3. Tom invented 35 riddles last night.

    4. Betty told jokes until bedtime.

    5. Bill imagined a monster under his bed.

    6. Dad bought new puzzles at the toy store.

Do All Sentences Have Direct Objects?

Since direct objects complete or receive the action of a verb, you only find direct objects after action verbs. Remember that there are two kinds of action verbs: physical and mental. In the sentences above, which action verbs show physical action?

Since being verbs do not show action, sentences with being verbs cannot have direct objects.

Not even all sentences with action verbs automatically have direct objects.

If you don't get a logical answer when you ask, "Whom?" or "What?" about the action verb, the sentence does not have a direct object. See Sentence 1, for example. If there is a logical answer, as in Sentence 2, it is the direct object.

Name _____   Date _____

Try It

Write three sentences. Make sure each one has an action verb and a direct object.

1. _____

2. _____

3. _____

Name _____   Date _____

Get Ready

Subject Complements and Direct Objects

A *subject complement* is a noun, pronoun, or adjective that follows and completes the meaning of a linking verb in a sentence. The subject complement identifies, explains, or describes the subject.

A *direct object* is a noun or pronoun that completes the meaning or receives the action of an action verb. To find a direct object in a sentence, ask, "Whom?" or "What?" about the action verb.

How Are They Similar?

Subject complements and direct objects have much in common, as you can see from this chart:

Subject Complement	Direct Object
• is a noun, pronoun, or adjective	• is a noun or pronoun
• appears in the predicate	• appears in the predicate
• follows the verb	• follows the verb
• completes the verb's meaning	• completes the verb's meaning

How Are They Different?

On the other hand, subject complements and direct objects are very different in certain ways, as you can see from this chart:

Subject Complement	Direct Object
• appears only after a linking verb	• appears only after an action verb
• completes the meaning of a linking verb	• completes the meaning or receives the action of an action verb
• identifies, explains, or describes the subject	• has something done to it by the subject
• is somehow the same as the subject	• is not the same as the subject

Name _____   Date _____

Try It

Use the word bank of nouns to complete each sentence. Fill in the blank before each sentence with SC if the noun you add is a subject complement, and DO if the noun you add is a direct object.

Word Bank: bodies   eggs   antennae   insects
                   butterfly   wings   cocoon   metamorphosis

Example:
<u>DO</u>   Butterflies change their <u>bodies</u> as they develop.

_____ 1. The name of this change is _____.

_____ 2. When the time is right, every caterpillar forms a _____.

_____ 3. Eventually, we see a _____ emerging from the cocoon.

_____ 4. Butterflies are _____.

Name _____   Date _____

Get Ready

Parts of Speech Review

You have learned six parts of speech. They are:

nouns   adjectives
pronouns   adverbs
verbs   conjunctions

Review what each part of speech does.

Prepositions

Now let's learn about a new part of speech: the *preposition*.

Prepositions are important, and they are everywhere! A preposition is a word that relates a noun or pronoun to some other word in the sentence.

Prepositions can point out time, place, direction, and relationship. Watch how the meanings of these sentences change when the underlined preposition changes.

I live <u>near</u> the river.   I live <u>on</u> the river.   I live <u>in</u> the river.
I live <u>for</u> the river.   I live <u>toward</u> the river.   I live <u>by</u> the river.

Study this list of common prepositions. You probably know them all and use many of them daily.

at   near   to
by   of   with
for   on   without
from   onto
in   over
into   through

Objects of Prepositions and Prepositional Phrases

A preposition relates a noun or pronoun to some other word in a sentence. This noun or pronoun follows the preposition, completes its meaning, and is called the *object of the preposition*.

A *phrase* is a group of related words. A *prepositional phrase* is a group of words that begins with a preposition, and usually ends with the noun or pronoun that is the object of the preposition.

Here are some examples of prepositional phrases. The prepositions are underlined once, and the objects of prepositions are underlined twice.

over my town   through the long tunnel   by today
from him   into great danger   with us

Name _____ Date _____

Try It

Each item below is a prepositional phrase. Underline the preposition once and underline the object of the preposition twice.

Example: <u>without </u>my <u>boots</u>

1. in her hair

2. with difficulty

3. to Canada

4. onto the old lady

5. at Dave's house

Name _____   Date _____

Get Ready

When a child builds a castle with blocks, she uses different shapes for different purposes. Rectangles and squares are good for walls, semicircles and triangles make nice decorations, and cylinders work well as columns.

Nouns are like building blocks because they help build sentences. And, like the blocks, nouns can serve different purposes depending on how they are used in each sentence.

So far you have learned that nouns can act as:

_____ subject
_____ subject complement
_____ direct object
_____ object of a preposition
_____ direct address

Match the items below with the proper role of a noun above. Fill in the blanks in front of the appropriate role with the letters of the items below.

Fill in the blanks above with
a. To find it, ask "Who?" or "What?" after an action verb.
b. To find it, ask "Who?" or "What?" before the verb.
c. It completes the meaning of the linking verb.
d. It receives the action of a verb.
e. It shows that someone is being spoken to directly.
f. It is who or what the sentence is about.
g. It identifies, explains, or describes the subject.
h. It is the name of a word that describes the person spoken to.
i. It follows a preposition and completes its meaning.

Name _____   Date _____

Try It

Analyze these three sentences by answering the following questions.

Sentence Analysis Questions
1. Is it a sentence or a fragment?
2. What kind of sentence is it?
3. What is the verb?
4. What is the simple subject?
5. Is there a direct object?
6. Are there any modifiers?
7. What part of speech is each word?

1. Jenny's big sister is a jewelry designer in New York.

Sentence or fragment?   _____

Kind of sentence?   _____

Verb?   _____

Simple subject?   _____

Direct object or
subject complement?   _____

Modifiers?   _____

Parts of speech?

Jenny's	_____	jewelry	_____
big	_____	designer	_____
sister	_____	in	_____
is	_____	New York	_____
a	_____		

2. Ted will put the dirty clothes into the laundry hamper now.

Sentence or fragment? _____

Kind of sentence? _____

Verb? _____

Simple subject? _____

Direct object or
subject complement? _____

Modifiers? _____

Parts of speech?

Ted	_____	into	_____
will put	_____	the	_____
the	_____	laundry	_____
dirty	_____	hamper	_____
clothes	_____	now	_____

3. You are a fine flute player, Edward!

Sentence or fragment? _____

Kind of sentence? _____

Verb? _____

Simple subject? _____

Direct object or
subject complement? _____

Modifiers? _____

Parts of speech?

You	_____	flute	_____
are	_____	player	_____
a	_____	Edward	_____
fine	_____		

Name _____   Date _____

Try It

Let's review what you have studied about nouns and how they work in sentences. Circle the letter of the correct answer.

1. What is a simple subject?
   a. the noun or pronoun in the subject that names who or what the sentence is about
   b. all the words that explain who or what the sentence is about

2. The Taj Mahal and St. Peter's Basilica are famous <u>buildings</u>.
   The underlined noun is an example of a(n):
   a. subject
   b. subject complement
   c. direct object
   d. object of a preposition

3. Karen saw the <u>Taj Mahal</u> when she went to India, and Frank visited <u>St. Peter's Basilica</u> in Rome.

   The underlined nouns are examples of:
   a. subjects
   b. subject complements
   c. direct objects
   d. objects of prepositions

4. Karen saw the Taj Mahal when she went to <u>India</u>, and Frank visited St. Peter's Basilica in <u>Rome</u>.
   The underlined nouns are examples of:
   a. subjects
   b. subject complements
   c. direct objects
   d. objects of prepositions

5. <u>Brazil </u>is a country with many colorful carnivals.
   The underlined noun is an example of a(n):
   a. subject
   b. subject complement
   c. direct object
   d. object of a preposition

6. Brazil is a <u>country </u>with many colorful carnivals.
   The underlined noun is an example of a(n):
   a. subject
   b. subject complement
   c. direct object
   d. object of a preposition

7. Brazil is a country with many colorful <u>carnivals</u>.
   The underlined noun is an example of a(n):
   a. subject
   b. subject complement
   c. direct object
   d. object of a preposition

8. Which of the following nouns is <u>not </u>a singular possessive form?
   a. cups
   b. girl's
   c. box's
   d. class's

9. Which of the following nouns is <u>not </u>a plural possessive form?
   a. babies'
   b. mosses'
   c. feet's
   d. tree's

10. Which of the following does <u>not</u> describe a prepositional phrase?
    a. begins with a preposition
    b. usually ends with a noun that is the object of the preposition
    c. always follows a linking verb
    d. shows time, place, direction, or relationship

11. Which word is <u>not</u> a preposition?
    a. onto
    b. the
    c. by
    d. for

12. A linking verb acts like_____between a subject and its subject complement.
    a. an equal sign
    b. a plus sign
    c. a minus sign
    d. a stop sign

13. Do linking verbs show action?
    a. yes
    b. no
    c. sometimes

14. Which of the following is <u>not</u> a linking verb?
    a. am
    b. are
    c. ate
    d. is

Name _____ Date _____

Get Ready

A sentence has a subject and a predicate. Only certain personal pronouns can be used as subjects in sentences. Do you remember which ones?

Look at the following sentences. The subjects are underlined for you. Put a check (✓) next to the ones that use the correct personal pronouns as subjects.

1. _____ <u>I</u> will learn how to water ski.
2. _____ <u>Me</u> will learn how to water ski.

3. _____ <u>You</u> are taking scuba diving lessons instead.

4. _____ <u>Him</u> is going to sit on the patio and read a book.
5. _____ <u>He</u> is going to sit on the patio and read a book.

6. _____ <u>She</u> plans to take a swim class.
7. _____ <u>Her</u> plans to take a swim class.

8. _____ <u>It</u> is a beautiful day to be outdoors.

9. _____ <u>We</u> will have lunch at the restaurant.
10. _____ <u>Us</u> will have lunch at the restaurant.

11. _____ <u>Them</u> will join us for supper.
12. _____ <u>They</u> will join us for supper.

As you probably remembered, the subject personal pronouns are:

   I   you   he   she   it   we   they

Name _____   Date _____

Try It

Analyze these three sentences by answering the following questions.

Sentence Analysis Questions
1. Is it a sentence or a fragment?
2. What kind of sentence is it?
3. What is the verb?
4. What is the simple subject?
5. Is there a direct object?
6. Are there any modifiers?
7. What part of speech is each word?

1. The cruel soldier stared coldly at little Mulan.

Sentence or fragment? _____

Kind of sentence? _____

Verb? _____

Simple subject? _____

Direct object or
subject complement? _____

Modifiers? _____

Parts of speech?

The	_____	coldly	_____
cruel	_____	at	_____
soldier	_____	little	_____
stared	_____	Mulan	_____

2. Now I will go to war in Father's place!

Sentence or fragment? _____

Kind of sentence? _____

Verb? _____

Simple subject? _____

Direct object or
subject complement? _____

Modifiers? _____

Parts of speech?

Now	_____	war	_____
I	_____	in	_____
will go	_____	Father's	_____
to	_____	place	_____

3. Brave Mulan was a hero for one thousand years.

Sentence or fragment? _____

Kind of sentence? _____

Verb? _____

Simple subject? _____

Direct object or
subject complement? _____

Modifiers? _____

Parts of speech?

Brave	_____	hero	_____
Mulan	_____	for	_____
was	_____	one thousand	_____
a	_____	years	_____

Name _____   Date _____

Get Ready

Personal Pronouns as Subject Complements

Remember that a *complement* fills up, balances, or completes something else. For example, a hand and a glove or a lock and a key are complements.

A *subject complement* follows and completes the meaning of a *linking verb* in a sentence. The subject complement identifies, explains, or describes the subject. Subject complements are often nouns or pronouns.

Subject complements refer directly to subjects. If you use a pronoun as a subject complement, you must use one of the subject pronouns:

I	you	he	she	it	we	they

Subjects = Subject Complements

Only sentences with linking verbs can have subject complements. Linking verbs, as their name implies, link or connect subjects and complements. They do not show action. The most common linking verbs are forms of the verb to *be:*

am	is	are	was	were
will be	shall be	have been	has been	had been

A linking verb acts like an equals sign, showing how the subject and subject complement are the same.

The best basketball player is you.
The best basketball player = you.

Name _____   Date _____

Try It

Rotate and Check!

You have learned that you must use subject pronouns in subject complements. It is helpful to memorize the subject pronouns. Rotating the subject and subject complement of a sentence with a linking verb can help you decide whether the personal pronoun in the complement is correct.

Read the sentences aloud the way they are. Next, say them aloud rotating the subject complement and the subject. Then put a check (✓) next to the sentences that have the correct pronoun in the subject complement.

Example: The star of the play was he.
               He was the star of the play.

____ 1. The lady in the red dress was she.
____ 2. The loudest person there was me.
____ 3. The best person for the job will be he.
____ 4. My oldest friend is you.
____ 5. The spectators were them.
____ 6. It is I.
____ 7. The driver of the bus has been her.
____ 8. The choir singers were they.
____ 9. The person you want is him.
____ 10. A very merry bunch are we.

Name _____   Date _____

Get Ready

Review

A subject complement follows and completes the meaning of a linking verb in a sentence. The subject complement identifies, explains, or describes the subject. Subject complements can be nouns, pronouns, or adjectives.

If you use a personal pronoun as a subject complement, you must use one of the subject personal pronouns:

I	you	he	she	it	we	they

Only sentences with linking verbs can have subject complements. Linking verbs connect subjects and complements instead of showing action. The most common linking verbs are forms of *be:*

am	is	are	was	were
will be	shall be	have been	has been	had been

A linking verb acts like an equal sign, showing how the subject and subject complement balance each other.

That mountain climber halfway up is she.
That mountain climber halfway up = she.

Sentence Rotation

It can be tricky to use personal pronouns as subject complements. One way to do it correctly is to memorize which personal pronouns are the subject forms.

Another helpful technique is sentence rotation, in which you rotate a sentence with a pronoun subject complement around its linking verb. That is, you flip the sentence so that the pronoun subject complement becomes the subject. The meaning of the sentence will not change, but if you have used an object pronoun by mistake, the rotated sentence should make the mistake easy to see. For example,

My grandparents' visiting nurse had been <u>him</u>.

Sound all right? Hmm . . . maybe. Let's rotate it to be sure:

<u>Him</u> had been my grandparents' visiting nurse.

No, that definitely doesn't sound right! *Him* is an object pronoun, not a subject pronoun. The sentence should read:

<u>He</u> had been my grandparents' visiting nurse.

And so, flip it one more time to return the pronoun to the subject complement position:

My grandparents' visiting nurse had been <u>he</u>.

By the way, only linking verb sentences can be rotated and still keep the same meaning. Don't try sentence rotation with action verb sentences, because you'll get nonsense! For example,

George ate an entire pizza.
An entire pizza ate George.

Name _____   Date _____

Try It

Underline the pronouns used as subject complements in these sentences. If the subject complement is an object pronoun instead of a subject pronoun, correct it on the line.

Hint: Not every sentence has a subject complement. Remember that subject complements only follow linking verbs.

_____ 1. The old father of three princesses was he.

_____ 2. The sisters with grand but false words were them.

_____ 3. The daughter with the most love was she.

_____ 4. The king abandoned her in the woods.

_____ 5. Father, look closely! It is me, your youngest daughter!

Name _____   Date _____

Get Ready

When a sentence has an action verb, it may also have a *direct object*. A direct object is a noun or pronoun that completes the meaning of an action verb. A direct object receives the action of a verb. To find a direct object in a sentence, ask, "Whom?" or "What?" after the action verb.

What is the direct object of this sentence?

1. Mr. Solvang hired me to cut his lawn this summer.

Not all sentences have direct objects. Sentences with linking verbs do not have them. Even sentences with action verbs do not automatically have direct objects.

If you ask, "Whom?" or "What?" after the action verb and get no logical answer, the sentence does not have a direct object. If there is a logical answer, it is the direct object.

Does this sentence have a direct object?

2. Mr. Solvang advertised in the neighborhood monthly paper.

Only certain personal pronouns can be used as direct objects. They are:

    me   you   him   her   it   us   them

Name _____   Date _____

Try It

Analyze these three sentences by answering the following questions.

Sentence Analysis Questions
1. Is it a sentence or a fragment?
2. What kind of sentence is it?
3. What is the verb?
4. What is the simple subject?
5. Is there a direct object?
6. Are there any modifiers?
7. What part of speech is each word?

1. Dionysius lived unhappily in a palace with many beautiful things.

Sentence or fragment? _____

Kind of sentence? _____

Verb? _____

Simple subject? _____

Direct object or
subject complement? _____

Modifiers? _____

Parts of speech?

Dionysius	_____	palace	_____
lived	_____	with	_____
unhappily	_____	many	_____
in	_____	beautiful	_____
a	_____	things	_____

2. Damocles, you will have my life for one day and one night.

Sentence or fragment? _____

Kind of sentence? _____

Verb? _____

Simple subject? _____

Direct object or
subject complement? _____

Modifiers? _____

Parts of speech?

Damocles	_____	one	_____
you	_____	day	_____
will have	_____	and	_____
my	_____	one	_____
life	_____	night	_____
for	_____		

3. The sword was a constant threat to his life.

Sentence or fragment? _____

Kind of sentence? _____

Verb? _____

Simple subject? _____

Direct object or
subject complement? _____

Modifiers? _____

Parts of speech?

The	_____	threat	_____
sword	_____	to	_____
was	_____	his	_____
a	_____	life	_____
constant	_____		

Name _____   Date _____

Get Ready

Prepositions and Objects of Prepositions

Prepositions can point out time, place, direction, and relationship. Prepositions relate a noun or pronoun to some other word in a sentence. The noun or pronoun follows the preposition, completes its meaning, and is called the *object of the preposition*.

Study this list of common prepositions:

across	into	through
at	near	to
behind	of	toward
by	on	under
for	onto	with
from	over	without
in		

Prepositional Phrases

A group of related words is a *phrase*. A preposition, the object of the preposition, and any modifiers of the object make up a *prepositional phrase*.

Find the prepositional phrases in these sentences. Underline the prepositions once and the object of the prepositions twice.

1. The airplane flew onto the runway.

2. The cows munched grass near the grain silo.

3. The skydiver turned toward the coast and jumped.

4. The passengers departed from the busy terminal.

5. Clouds raced across the sky.

Personal Pronouns as Objects of Prepositions

Personal pronouns can substitute for nouns, but certain forms have to be used in certain ways. For example, you know that *I, you, he, she, it, we,* and *they* are the subject forms of the personal pronouns. The object forms of the personal pronoun are:

me   you   him   her   it   us   them

As you can probably guess, when personal pronouns are objects of prepositions, you must use their object forms. Choose a different object pronoun to complete each prepositional phrase in the sentences below.

6. My brother jumped over _____ last night.

7. The helicopter flew under _____.

8. Toward _____ came a horrible sound

9. She looked under _____ and laughed.

10. I'll never read another story by _____ again.

Name _____   Date _____

Try It

Select five prepositions from the Word Bank. For each one, write a sentence with a prepositional phrase. Underline the prepositional phrase. Use a personal pronoun for the object of the preposition.

Hint: Prepositional phrases begin with prepositions and end with objects of the preposition.

Word Bank

across	from	on	toward
at	in	onto	under
behind	into	over	with
by	near	through	without
for	of	to	

1. _____

2. _____

3. _____

4. _____

5. _____

Name _____   Date _____

Get Ready

Let's review what you have learned about pronouns and the words they work with in sentences. Circle the correct answer to each item below.

1. A pronoun
   a. can take the place of a noun.
   b. is another name for a professional noun.

2. Nouns can be subjects, subject complements, direct objects, or objects of prepositions. That means that pronouns can be
   a. whatever they want to be.
   b. subjects, subject complements, direct objects, or objects of prepositions.

3. The subject pronouns are
   a. me, you, him, her, it, us, and them.
   b. I, you, he, she, it, we, and they.

4. The object pronouns are
   a. me, you, him, her, it, us, and them.
   b. I, you, he, she, it, we, and they.

5. Subject pronouns are used as
   a. subjects and subject complements.
   b. direct objects and objects of prepositions.

6. Object pronouns are used as
   a. subjects and subject complements.
   b. direct objects and objects of prepositions.

7. Subject complements always follow
   a. an action verb.
   b. the leader.
   c. a linking verb.

8. Direct objects always follow
   a. an action verb.
   b. a linking verb
   c. their dreams.

9. Objects of prepositions always come somewhere after a(n)
   a. object
   b. preposition

10. The most common linking verbs are forms of the verb
    a. take
    b. love
    c. read
    d. be

Name _____   Date _____

Try It

Show what you have learned about pronouns and the roles they play in sentences. Under each heading below, write two sentences. Each sentence should use a different personal pronoun from the Word Bank.

Word Bank

I, me	it
you	we, us
he, him	they, them
she, her	

Sentences with personal pronouns as subjects:

1. _____

2. _____

Sentences with personal pronouns as subject complements:

3. _____

4. _____

Sentences with personal pronouns as direct objects:

5. _____

6. _____

Sentences with personal pronouns as objects of prepositions:

7. _____

8. _____

Name _____   Date _____

Get Ready

Since pronouns can take the place of nouns, they are like nouns in many ways.

Nouns and pronouns have *number*. In grammar, number doesn't refer to 8, or 127, or 3 million. Number refers to singular and plural. If a word refers to one, it is *singular*; if it refers to more than one, it is *plural*.

Singular Personal Pronouns	Plural Personal Pronouns
I, me	we, us
you	you
he, him; she, her; it	they, them

1. Which of the singular personal pronouns are subject forms?

   _____

2. Which of the plural personal pronouns are object forms?

   _____

3. Which personal pronoun is the same in the singular and the plural?

   _____

Name _____   Date _____

Try It

Analyze these three sentences by answering the following questions.

Sentence Analysis Questions
1. Is it a sentence or a fragment?
2. What kind of sentence is it?
3. What is the verb?
4. What is the simple subject?
5. Is there a direct object or subject complement?
6. Are there any modifiers?
7. What part of speech is each word?

1. Everywhere St. George saw men busy in the fields, women at work in their homes, and little children at play.

Sentence or fragment?   _____

Kind of sentence?   _____

Verb?   _____

Simple subject?   _____

Direct object or
subject complement?   _____

Modifiers?   _____

Parts of speech?

Everywhere	_____	work	_____
St. George	_____	in	_____
saw	_____	their	_____
men	_____	homes	_____
busy	_____	and	_____
in	_____	little	_____
the	_____	children	_____
fields	_____	at	_____
women	_____	play	_____
at			

2. One breath of the terrible dragon will destroy you, Sir Knight!

Sentence or fragment? _____

Kind of sentence? _____

Verb? _____

Simple subject? _____

Direct object or
subject complement? _____

Modifiers? _____

Parts of speech?

One	_____	dragon	_____
breath	_____	will destroy	_____
of	_____	you	_____
the	_____	Sir Knight	_____
terrible	_____		

3. St. George was a great defender of the princess and of her people.

Sentence or fragment? _____

Kind of sentence? _____

Verb? _____

Simple subject? _____

Direct object or
subject complement? _____

Modifiers? _____

Parts of speech?

St. George	_____	the	_____
was	_____	princess	_____
a	_____	and	_____
great	_____	of	_____
defender	_____	her	_____
of	_____	people	_____

Name _____   Date _____

Get Ready

Person Speaking, Person Spoken To, Person Spoken About
A personal pronoun can name:

1. The *speaker or speakers*: *I, me, we*, and *us*. For example,

    Singular   *I* am very sleepy.
                    Mom gave *me* a new alarm clock.

    Plural   *We* are going to bed early tonight.
                    Dad got *us* some warm pajamas.

2. The person or persons *spoken to*: *you*. For example,

    Singular or Plural   *You* like to take chances.
                          Trouble never seems to find *you,* though.

3. The persons, places, things, or ideas *spoken about*: *he, him, she, her, it, they*, and *them*. For example,

    Singular   *He* knows how to bowl very well.
                    Has his uncle ever seen *him* bowl?

                    She goes camping on weekends.
                    Beth would like to go with *her* someday.

                    It is not a nice day outside.
                    What can anyone do about *it*?

    Plural   *They* asked Ed to feed their 13 cats.
                    Ed hopes to find all of *them*!

First Person, Second Person, Third Person

"Person speaking," "person spoken to," and "person spoken about" are useful ways to remember who or what personal pronouns name.

But here is a shortcut way to label pronouns by who or what they name: *first person*, *second person*, and *third person*. Here are the new and old names, side by side:

New Name		Old Name
First Person	=	Person(s) Speaking or Speaker(s)
Second Person	=	Person(s) Spoken To
Third Person	=	Person(s), Place(s), Thing(s) Spoken About

Summary

Study the chart below, which groups personal pronouns by:

1. *person* (first, second, or third)
2. *number* (singular or plural)
3. *subject* and *object* forms

	Singular		Plural	
	Subject	Object	Subject	Object
First Person	I	me	we	us
Second Person	you	you	you	you
Third Person	he, she, it	him, her, it	they	them

Name _____   Date _____

Try It

Write the person and number for each pronoun listed below.
Bonus: Is it the subject or object form of the pronoun?

Examples, with bonus:
    she   third person, singular, subject
    you   second person, singular or plural, subject or object

1. me _____

2. them _____

3. we _____

4. us _____

5. I _____

6. her _____

7. he _____

8. it _____

9. they _____

10. him _____

Name _____ Date _____

Get Ready

Personal Pronoun Review
Circle the answer to each question.

1. To say that a personal pronoun has <u>number </u>means
   a. 555-1212
   b. singular or plural
   c. first person, second person, third person

2. To say that a personal pronoun has <u>person </u>means
   a. first, second, and third person, which tell who the pronoun
      names: the speaker, the person spoken to, or the person
      spoken about
   b. first, second, and third person, which tell whether the
      pronoun is singular or plural
   c. first, second, and third person, which tell whether the
      pronoun should come first, second, or third in the sentence

3. Which of these pronouns is <u>not </u>first person?
   a. I   c.   me
   b. us   d.   you

4. Which of these pronouns is <u>not </u>third person?
   a. he   c.   you
   b. they   d.   it

5. Which of these pronouns is <u>not </u>plural?
   a. we   c.   they
   b. she   d.   them

Gender

Personal pronouns also have *gender*. Gender classifies things—in this case, words—by sex: *masculine*, *feminine*, or *neuter*.

Masculine gender means male:
Abraham Lincoln, Robin Hood, Billy Robinson

Feminine gender means female:
Sandra Day O'Connor, Queen Elizabeth, Sally Jones

Neuter gender means that it is neither masculine nor feminine. It usually describes things and places:
refrigerator, Alaska, bike, skyscraper

Some nouns can be either masculine or feminine, depending on the specific person or animal being talked about:
cat, traveler, worker, bird, driver

What is the gender of each of these nouns?

6. Mr. Pozzi _____

7. pizza _____

8. zookeeper _____

9. Zelda Mary Mazza _____

10. zebra _____

Gender in Personal Pronouns

Like many nouns, most personal pronouns can be masculine, feminine, or both. The gender of the pronoun depends on the gender of who or what is speaking, spoken to, or spoken about.

The pronouns that can be masculine, feminine, or both are:

I   me   you   we   us   they   them

You can see how this works in these sentences:
"I want you to show me that flip," said Ricky to Bess.
"I will if you'll teach me to cartwheel," replied Bess to Ricky.

I and *me* are masculine when Ricky is speaking, but feminine when Bess is speaking. *You* is feminine when Ricky uses it to refer to Bess, but masculine when Bess uses it to refer to Ricky.

In addition to being masculine, feminine, or both, *they* and *them* can also refer to neuter nouns. For example,
Architects design buildings and then help construct them.

But third person singular pronouns are different, because they have three specific gender forms:
masculine   he, him
feminine: she, her
neuter: it

You can use *he* or *him* only for a male, *she* or *her* only for a female, and *it* only for something neuter.

Name _____   Date _____

Try It

Write one personal pronoun that fits each description.

Bonus: Include and label <u>both </u>the subject and the object forms for each pronoun described. Remember that the subject and object forms of some pronouns are the same.

Examples:
    second person, singular: you
    third person, plural: they

Examples, with bonus:
    second person, singular: you (subject), you (object)
    third person, plural: they (subject), them (object)

1. first person, plural   _____

2. third person, singular, masculine   _____

3. third person, singular, neuter   _____

4. first person, singular   _____

5. second person, plural   _____

6. third person, singular, feminine   _____

Name _____   Date _____

Get Ready

Possessive Pronouns

If you possess something, you own it. *Possessive pronouns* show ownership.

The possessive pronouns are *mine, ours, yours, his, hers, its,* and *theirs.* Since they come from personal pronouns, possessive pronouns have person, number, and gender.

Study this chart of the possessive pronouns.

Pronoun	Person and Number	Gender	Example
mine	first person singular	depends on speaker	That dog is mine.
ours	first person plural	depends on speakers	A bad dog bit ours.
yours	second person singular or plural	depends on who is spoken to	Yours is at the kennel.
his	third person singular	masculine	His hid in the doghouse.
hers	third person singular	feminine	Fifi sees hers chew a bone.
its	third person singular	neuter	The bone is its.
theirs	third person plural	depends on who is spoken about	Has anyone seen theirs?

Personal Pronouns in Contractions

If something contracts, it shortens or becomes smaller. A *contraction* is a short form of a word or group of words.

Most contractions are formed from two words. If you combine a pronoun and a verb, some letters drop out of the verb. An apostrophe marks the place where the letters dropped out.

What are the contractions for these pronoun-verb combinations?

1. she will   __she'll_____

2. you are   __you're_____

3. they would   __they'd_____

4. he has   __he's_____

5. we have   __we've_____

6. I am   __I'm_____

7. it is   __it's_____

Name _____   Date _____

Get Ready

Introduction

Now it's time for two new kinds of pronouns: *reflexive* pronouns and *intensive* pronouns.

Reflexive and intensive pronouns have different jobs in sentences, but they look identical. Read over the chart of reflexive and intensive pronouns below. How are they similar to personal pronouns? How are they different?

Reflexive and Intensive Pronouns

	Singular	Plural
First Person	myself	ourselves
Second Person	yourself	yourselves
Third Person	himself herself itself	themselves

Reflexive Pronouns

The job of a *reflexive pronoun* is to refer back to another noun in a sentence, usually the subject. One meaning of the word *reflexive* is *reflecting back*. The sentences below illustrate how reflexive pronouns do that.

Isaiah rowed himself across Green Lake.

The children agreed among themselves.

You trained yourselves very well at sports camp.

I accidentally bit myself instead of the hamburger.

Look at the two underlined words in each sentence. Do they refer to the same people? The reflexive pronouns, which you usually find after the verb, are reflections of the subjects.

Since a reflexive pronoun typically *refers back* to the subject of a sentence, a reflexive pronoun can never *be* the subject. A reflexive pronoun will be an object or a subject complement.

Intensive Pronouns

Intensive pronouns don't exactly replace another noun or pronoun. They *place emphasis on* or *intensify* another noun or pronoun partner. In the sentences below the intensive pronoun is underlined, and the noun or pronoun it emphasizes is in italics.

The *duchess* herself shook Mom's hand.

The *outfit* itself is not the problem; it's how you look in it.

My brothers tell us to be quiet, but *they* themselves are loud!

You should make your bed yourself.

As you can see from the examples, an intensive pronoun often, though not always, follows immediately after the partner noun or pronoun it emphasizes.

Name_____   Date_____

Try It

Write four sentences: two with reflexive pronouns, and two with intensive pronouns.

Underline and label the pronouns as reflexive or intensive.
For reflexives, draw arrows back to and underline the subjects they reflect.
For intensives, draw arrows back to and underline their partner nouns or pronouns.

1. _____

2. _____

3. _____

4. _____

Name _____   Date _____

Try It

Let's review pronouns. Match the numbered items with the correct lettered descriptions. Items marked (2) have two matching descriptions. One of the lettered descriptions will be used more than once.

_____ 1.   first person (2)
_____ 2.   second person (2)
_____ 3.   third person (2)
_____ 4.   number
_____ 5.   plural
_____ 6.   singular
_____ 7.   gender
_____ 8.   masculine
_____ 9.   feminine
_____ 10. neuter
_____ 11. possessive pronoun (2)
_____ 12. reflexive pronoun (2)
_____ 13. intensive pronoun (2)

a.   means classification as singular or plural
b.   reflects back to the subject
c.   means classification by sex
d.   examples are *I, me, we, us, mine, myself, ourselves*
e.   refers to the person(s) spoken to
f.   refers to one
g.   refers to the speaker or speakers
h.   refers to more than one
i.   describes males
j.   refers to the person(s) spoken about
k.   examples are *you, yours, yourself, yourselves*
l.   describes females

m. ends in *-self* or *-selves*

n. describes things that are neither male nor female

o. pronoun that shows ownership

p. examples are *mine, yours, his, hers, its, ours, theirs*

q. emphasizes another noun or pronoun

r. examples include *he, her, it, they, them, his, hers, theirs, itself, themselves*

Name _____ Date _____

Get Ready

Identifying Adjectives

Which parts of speech do adjectives modify, or describe?

1. _____

2. _____

Write five adjectives.

3. _____

4. _____

5. _____

6. _____

7. _____

Adjectives often come before the words they modify. One kind of adjective answers the question, "What kind?" Write adjectives that tell *what kind* to complete sentences 8–10. Don't use any of the adjectives you used in 3–7 above.

8. Heidi has a(n) _____ desk.

9. The _____ restaurant opens at 5 a.m.

10. My parakeet is a(n) _____ bird.

Proper Adjectives

As their name suggests, *proper adjectives* come from proper nouns. Like proper nouns, proper adjectives are capitalized. These adjectives are "proper" because they describe *specific named* persons, places, things, or ideas.

Perhaps the most common proper adjectives are those formed from place names. Study this list of examples.

Proper Noun	Proper Adjective
America	American
Norway	Norwegian
Brazil	Brazilian
France	French
Hawaii	Hawaiian
Paris	Parisian
East	Eastern

After you have completed your workbook practice on adjectives, return to the Student Guide to learn how to diagram sentences.

Name _____   Date _____

Try It

Sentence Diagramming Steps

1. **Verb?**
   Write the verb on the main diagram line.

2. **Subject?**
   Write the subject in front of the verb on the main diagram line. Draw a short vertical line (that cuts through the main line) to separate the subject and the verb.

3. **Direct object or subject complement, if any?**
   Write the direct object or subject complement after the verb on the main diagram line. Draw a short vertical (for direct object) or slanted (for subject complement) line to separate the direct object or the subject complement from the verb.

4. **Verb modifiers, if any?**
   Write the modifiers on slanted lines below the verb.

5. **Subject modifiers, if any?**
   Write the modifiers on slanted lines below the subject.

6. **Direct object or subject complement modifiers, if any?**
   Write the modifiers on slanted lines below the direct object or subject complement.

Diagram these three sentences. You will be guided through the steps.

1. Sentence diagrams are fun.

2. Many children love and enjoy diagrams.

3. My friends and I prefer soccer games!

Name _____ Date _____

Get Ready

Articles—three little words that we use every day—are adjectives.
In English, the articles are *a*, *an*, and *the*.

Articles are adjectives because they describe a noun. *A* and *an*
are *indefinite* articles. *Indefinite* can mean *not specific.* Indefinite
articles indicate that a noun is any one of a *general* group or kind.

We use *a* before words that begin with a consonant sound, and *an*
before words that begin with a vowel sound. It is the first *sound*,
not the first *letter*, that tells you which article to use.

   <u>an</u> umbrella
   <u>a</u> fire hydrant
   <u>an</u> hour (Hour begins with a vowel sound even though the word
   starts with the letter *h.*)

The is the *definite article. Definite* can mean *specific*. The definite
article indicates that a noun is someone, someplace, or something
in particular.

<u>Indefinite (a, an)</u>   <u>Definite (the)</u>
Barb picked <u>a</u> flower.   Barb picked <u>the</u> flower.
<u>A</u> movie is playing in town.   <u>The</u> movie is playing in town.

Practice
Fill in each blank with the correct form of the article requested:
indefinite (*a, an*) or definite (*the*).

1. (definite) _____ locomotive

2. (indefinite) _____ umbrella

3. (definite) _____ hula hoop

4. (indefinite) _____ trapeze

Name _____   Date _____

Try It

Analyze and diagram these two sentences. Ask for help if you need it.

Sentence Analysis Questions

1. Sentence or fragment?
2. Kind of sentence?
3. Verb?
4. Simple subject?
5. Direct object or subject complement?
6. Modifiers?
7. Parts of speech?

Sentence Diagramming Steps

1. Verb?
Write the verb on the main diagram line.

2. Subject?
Write the subject in front of the verb on the main diagram line. Draw a short vertical line (that cuts through the main line) to separate the subject and the verb.

3. Direct object or subject complement, if any?
Write the direct object or subject complement after the verb on the main diagram line, with a short vertical (for direct object) or slanted (for subject complement) line between them.

4. Verb modifiers, if any?
Write the modifiers on slanted lines below the verb.

5. Subject modifiers, if any?
Write the modifiers on slanted lines below the subject.

6. Direct object or subject complement modifiers, if any?
Write the modifiers on slanted lines below the direct object or subject complement.

Sentences to Analyze and Diagram

1. Merry Robin Hood won the golden arrow.

Sentence or fragment? _____

Kind of sentence? _____

Verb? _____

Simple subject? _____

Direct object or
subject complement? _____

Modifiers? _____

Parts of speech?   Merry _____   the _____

Robin Hood _____   golden _____

won _____   arrow _____

Diagram:

2. One gold piece is a generous reward!

Sentence or fragment?   _____

Kind of sentence?   _____

Verb?   _____

Simple subject?   _____

Direct object or
subject complement?   _____

Modifiers?   _____

Parts of speech?

One	_____	a	_____
gold	_____	generous	_____
piece	_____	reward	_____
is	_____		

Diagram:

Name   Date

Get Ready

Demonstrative Adjectives

Demonstrative adjectives point out specific person(s), place(s), thing(s), or idea(s). *To demonstrate* can mean *to show*, and demonstrative adjectives show which one or ones. The demonstrative adjectives are:

Singular	Plural
this	these
that	those

This and *these* usually point to nouns that are nearby, or nearer than others. *That* and *those* usually point to nouns that are far away, or farther away than others.

This town is where I was born.
These potato chips are Mom's favorite kind.

Has Kevin ever gone swimming at that other beach?
Try on those red boots over there.

Possessive Adjectives

Possessive adjectives, which are formed from personal pronouns, show ownership. Like personal pronouns, possessive adjectives have person and number. They sometimes tell gender as well.

Study this list of possessive adjectives:

First Person
Singular:	my	(belongs to me)
Plural:	our	(belongs to us)

Second Person
Singular or Plural:	your	(belongs to you)

Third Person
Singular:	his	(masculine; belongs to him)
	her	(feminine; belongs to her)
	its	(neuter; belongs to it)
Plural:	their	(belongs to them)

When a possessive adjective modifies a noun, it indicates to whom the noun belongs. In these examples, the possessive adjective is underlined. Name the noun or nouns that each possessive adjective modifies.

1. My Grandpa is 100 years old. _____

2. Is your grandfather still alive? _____

3. His grandfather fought in World War II. _____

4. Her grandparents were dairy farmers. _____

5. Have you ever seen a 100-year-old man driving a convertible with its top down? _____

6. Our Grandpa and Grandma live in Missouri. _____

7. Their Granddad died in 1984. _____

Name _____ Date _____

Get Ready

Adjectives That Tell How Many or How Much

One way adjectives describe nouns is to tell *how many* or *how much*.

Some adjectives tell *exactly* how many or what number.

1. <u>Three</u> baseball players are sick this week.
2. In a week I will celebrate my <u>tenth</u> birthday.
3. Mr. Jossy swam <u>88</u> lengths of the pool.

Some adjectives tell *about* how many or how much, such as *much, several, all, most,* or *many.*

4. Tim planted <u>some</u> plants at the park clean-up day.
5. The sign says the shopkeeper will be back in a <u>few</u> hours.

Adjective Position in Sentences

Adjectives Before Nouns
You have probably noticed that adjectives often come before the nouns or pronouns they modify. In sentences 1-5 above, find and name the noun described by each underlined "how many" adjective.

1. _____

2. _____

3. _____

4. _____

5. _____

Adjectives After Linking Verbs

Adjectives that follow a linking verb and stand alone are subject complements. A subject complement completes the meaning of the linking verb and describes the sentence.

For example,
    Subject complements can be tricky.

In the sentence above, *tricky* is an adjective used as a subject complement. It follows the linking verb *can be*, and it describes *subject complements.*

Now it's your turn to find adjectives used as subject complements.

In sentences 6–8 below, do the following:
a. Box the subject.
b. Circle the linking verb.
c. Underline the adjective used as a subject complement.

6. After the rugby match, we were tired.

7. That house on the corner is old.

8. On her birthday, Jenna will be happy.

Name _____   Date _____

Get Ready

Three Degrees of Comparison

Adjectives also describe by *comparing*. Adjectives have three degrees, or levels, of comparison: positive, comparative, and superlative.

The *positive* degree of comparison is the basic building block. In fact, the positive degree doesn't really compare at all—it just describes. For example:

> Our minivan is dirty.
> That yellow apple looks rotten.

The *comparative* degree compares two nouns to one another. Comparative adjectives often end in *-er*, but sometimes they use the word *more*. For example:

> Our minivan is <u>dirtier</u> than yours.
> The brown apple looks <u>more rotten</u> than that yellow one.

The *superlative* degree compares three or more nouns to one another. Superlative adjectives often end in *-est*, but sometimes they use the word *most*. For example:

> Our minivan is the <u>dirtiest</u> vehicle on the whole street.
> The black apple is the <u>most rotten</u> of the three.

Forming Comparatives and Superlatives

How do you know when to add -er or use *more* to make a comparative adjective? How do you know when to add -est or use *most* to make a superlative adjective?

Often, you simply must choose what sounds right to you. But here are a few tips to help you decide:

One-syllable adjectives usually add -er to form the comparative and -est to form the superlative.

Positive	Comparative	Superlative
loud	louder	loudest
big	bigger	biggest

Two-syllable adjectives vary in how they form their comparatives and superlatives.

Positive	Comparative	Superlative
silly	sillier	silliest
careful	more careful	most careful

Adjectives of **three or more syllables** usually use *more* for the comparative and *most* for the superlative.

Positive	Comparative	Superlative
fortunate	more fortunate	most fortunate
difficult	more difficult	most difficult

Name _____   Date _____

Try It

Each sentence below contains a positive, comparative, or superlative adjective. Underline the adjective and label it **P** for positive degree, **C** for comparative degree, or **S** for superlative degree. Do not consider articles (*a, an, the*) as adjectives in this exercise.

Example:

__S__   The Fitzes have the greenest lawn on our street.

_____ 1. Who has the goofier laugh: Sally or Sibyl?

_____ 2. Becca sounds funny when she giggles.

_____ 3. When Jarred and Rina have face-making contests, Jarred looks crazier.

_____ 4. The strangest sound of all is George snorting and honking.

Name _____ Date _____

Get Ready

An Adjective Tale

Once upon a time, there was a friendly, interesting fellow named Adje C. Tive. Mr. Tive loved to describe things and spend time with his close friends, the nouns and pronouns. His friends called him "Common," because he enjoyed relaxing with every imaginable kind of noun and pronoun.

Mr. Tive's brother's nickname is "Proper." Unlike Common, who can have fun with almost anyone, Proper is very particular. A picky fellow, he spends time only with specific persons, places, and things. He is fond of capital letters.

The Tives have a very big and well-known family. Perhaps you have heard of some of them.

The three members of the Article family are very small and quiet— really, they're a little dull—and they depend completely on nouns to make things interesting.

Two of the Articles—A and An—are known as the Indefinite Twins. They are friends with any noun. A's pals are nouns that begin with consonants, and An feels more at home with nouns that begin with vowels.

Unlike her Indefinite Twin sisters, The is always very definite. She knows exactly whom or what she wants to be next to at all times. (The and Proper are alike in this way.) But, like the twins, she stays in the background and never interferes.

Some relatives, however, are not so well behaved. The Demonstratives, for example, are always pointing and waving, yelling:

"Here, this one!"
"No, that one! Look at these things!"
"Wait! What about those things over there?"

The Demonstratives are very helpful when you need to know which is which or what is what. However, they can be embarrassing because they never seem to remember that it's not polite to point.

Likewise, the Possessives have their unpleasant side. They think too much about who owns what and what belongs to whom. When you pass the Possessive house, you almost always hear an argument:

"Pass my waffle!"
"That's not your waffle, that's his waffle!"
"What? Who took your waffle?"
"Quiet! No arguments at my dinner table."
"It's not your table, it's their table."

And so on. If you need to settle a disagreement about ownership, the Possessives are valuable—but they can't do much else.

The large and hardworking Howmany family is very good with numbers. They have the information you want when you want it. The Howmany family has two branches: the Abouts and the Exactlys. You probably know many of them. Some famous Abouts include All, Many, Much, Both, Some, Every, and Few. And the Exactlys go on forever: One and his partner First, Two and Second, Three and Third, Four and Fourth—you get the idea.

The last Tive relatives are the Comparison trio: Positive, Comparative, and Superlative. Sometimes these three are a bit childish. You know the kind: every conversation turns into a contest. Listen at the Comparison door, and you'll hear something like this:

"I'm smart."
"Well, I'm smarter than you are."
"Ha! I'm the smartest of all."

And that's the story of Adje C. Tive and his family: Common, Proper, the Definite and Indefinite Articles, the Demonstratives, the Possessives, the Howmanys, and the Comparisons. Perhaps you have met them already.

Name _____ Date _____

Try It

What kind of adjective is the underlined word? Fill in the blanks with one of the following terms:

common   possessive   how many
proper   comparative   definite article
demonstrative   superlative   indefinite article

Examples:

_proper_____ Mrs. McCarty is <u>French</u>.

_definite article_____ <u>The</u> dangerous tornado didn't touch down here.

_____ 1. <u>Her</u> mother was kind to us.

_____ 2. That dog's fur is <u>softer</u> than my cat's.

_____ 3. Mr. Santiago is the <u>most talented</u> carpenter.

_____ 4. Eddie drank <u>six</u> bottles of juice after the game.

_____ 5. <u>These</u> shoes are too small for me.

Name _____ Date _____

Unit 6 Pretest

Part 1: Identifying Action Verbs
Underline the action verb in each sentence.

1. We cooked hamburgers and hot dogs on the grill.

2. Leaves fell from the maple tree.

3. My little brother rides a tricycle.

4. A thick fog covers the lake early in the morning.

5. Mark and Brad hiked along the mountain trail.

Part 2: Using Action Verbs in Sentences
Complete each sentence with an action verb.

6. Jason _____ his lunch box yesterday.

7. When the storm ended, we _____ in the puddles.

8. A small spider _____ across the bedroom floor.

9. Mom _____ when she tasted the breakfast we cooked for her.

10. Four kittens _____ in the cardboard box.

Unit 6 Pretest

Part 3: Using Forms of *Be* and *Do* in Sentences
Choose the correct form of the verb to complete each sentence. Fill in the bubble.

11. _____ you on the cleanup committee last year?
    - ⓐ Was
    - ⓑ Were

12. My grandmother's name _____ Charlotte.
    - ⓐ am
    - ⓑ is

13. The car _____ stuck in the drift of snow.
    - ⓐ was
    - ⓑ were

14. There _____ three pine trees in the backyard.
    - ⓐ is
    - ⓑ are

15. I _____ the youngest person in my family.
    - ⓐ am
    - ⓑ is

16. Your new jacket _____ look very comfortable.
    - ⓐ do
    - ⓑ does

17. The children _____ want to leave the carnival.
    - ⓐ don't
    - ⓑ doesn't

Unit 6 Pretest

18. _____ you think you can finish the race?
    ⓐ Do
    ⓑ Does

19. The car _____ have a spare tire.
    ⓐ don't
    ⓑ doesn't

20. _____ this puzzle have all of its pieces?
    ⓐ Do
    ⓑ Does

Name _____   Date _____

Get Ready

Read this list of action verbs:

sprint	snort	think	fly	listen
giggle	grasp	scream	nap	create

Sometimes the action is physical:
   sit, stand, jump, destroy, wash

Sometimes the action is mental:
   remember, forget, consider, feel

Powerful and appropriate action verbs can make writing more interesting. Use them when you can.

Exercises in English will give you more practice with action verbs.

Name _____ Date _____

Try It

Analyze and diagram these sentences. Ask for help if you need it.

Sentence Analysis Questions
1. Sentence or fragment?
2. Kind of sentence?
3. Verb?
4. Simple subject?
5. Direct object or subject complement?
6. Modifiers?
7. Parts of speech?

1. Old Solon was a wise lawmaker from Athens.

Sentence or fragment? _____

Kind of sentence? _____

Verb? _____

Simple subject? _____

Direct object or
subject complement? _____

Modifiers? _____

Parts of speech?   Old _____   wise _____
                    Solon _____ lawmaker _____
                    was _____   from _____
                    a _____   Athens _____

2. Death and destruction in the palace.

Sentence or fragment?   _____

Kind of sentence?   _____

Verb?   _____

Simple subject?   _____

Direct object or
subject complement?   _____

Modifiers?   _____

Parts of speech?

Death	_____	in	_____
and	_____	the	_____
destruction	_____	palace	_____

3. Cyrus of Babylon repented and returned the defeated Croesus to freedom.

Sentence or fragment?   _____

Kind of sentence?   _____

Verb?   _____

Simple subject?   _____

Direct object or
subject complement?   _____

Modifiers?   _____

Parts of speech?

Cyrus	_____	the	_____
of	_____	defeated	_____
Babylon	_____	Croesus	_____
repented	_____	to	_____
and	_____	freedom	_____
returned	_____		

Name _____   Date _____

Get Ready

Read this list of verbs:

is	are	was	were
will be	have been	has been	am
had been	being	been	

They are definitely not action verbs. Yet, they are very important because they express being, or existence. Think about it—we need to *be* before we can *do*, don't we? Being verbs may not seem exciting or energetic, but they are essential.

Turn to *Exercises in English* to practice using being verbs.

Name _____   Date _____

Try It

Sentence Diagramming Steps

1. Verb?
Write the verb on the main diagram line.

2. Subject?
Write the subject in front of the verb on the main diagram line. Draw a short vertical line (that cuts through the main line) to separate the subject and the verb.

3. Direct object or subject complement, if any?
Write the direct object or subject complement after the verb on the main diagram line. Draw a short vertical (for direct object) or slanted (for subject complement) line to separate it from the subject.

4. Verb modifiers, if any?
Write the modifiers on slanted lines below the verb.

5. Subject modifiers, if any?
Write the modifiers on slanted lines below the subject.

6. Direct object or subject complement modifiers, if any?
Write the modifiers on slanted lines below the direct object or subject complement.

Diagram these three sentences. Ask for help if you need it.

1. Paul Revere rowed a boat and rode a horse.

2. Charlestown and Concord were two colonial towns.

3. His words shall echo forevermore!

Name _____ Date _____

Get Ready

We often think of parts of speech as being one word. For example,

adjective:	sparkling
noun:	diamond
verb:	shines
adverb:	brightly

Sometimes, however, groups of related words can work together to do the job of one part of speech. Such groups of words are called *phrases*.

A *verb phrase* is a group of words that acts as one verb. A verb phrase is made up of one or more helping verbs and a main verb.

one or more helping verbs	+	main verb	=	verb phrase
am		shouting		am shouting
would		be		would be
do		taste		do taste
had been		writing		had been writing
shall have		lost		shall have lost

Auxiliary is an adjective that means "helping." Helping verbs are also called auxiliary verbs. You can think of the main verb as the boss and the auxiliary verbs as its helpers. One of the main jobs of an auxiliary verb is to help show the *tense*, or time, of the verb. For example,

present tense:	<u>am</u> singing, <u>do</u> sing
past tense:	<u>was</u> singing, <u>did</u> sing
future tense:	<u>will be</u> singing, <u>will</u> sing

Here are some common auxiliary verbs:

has	were	can
have	will	could
had	shall	would
is	may	should
am	do	must
are	does	ought
was	did	might

Even though the verbs on the list above are often used as helpers, some of them can also be main verbs. For example,

I <u>am</u> as hungry as a skinny wolf in winter.
Jenny <u>had</u> three cups of vanilla pudding after lunch.
Let's <u>do</u> our reports on hot-air ballooning now.

Name _____ Date _____

Try It

Write five sentences that use verb phrases. Underline the auxiliary verb or verbs, and circle the main verb.

Example: We <u>should have</u> (taken) our binoculars on our hike.

1. _____

2. _____

3. _____

4. _____

5. _____

Name _____   Date _____

Get Ready

Verb Phrase Review
Circle the letter of the correct answer.

1. A phrase is
   a. a helping verb or verbs + a main verb
   b. a group of words doing the job of one part of speech

2. A verb phrase is
   a. a helping verb or verbs + a main verb
   b. a verb with more than one meaning

3. An auxiliary verb is
   a. a main verb
   b. a helping verb

4. Which of the following is <u>not</u> a group of auxiliary verbs?
   a. stink, rub, wash, mow, cut
   b. will, have, did, is, may

Verb Phrases in Questions and Negative Statements
A *question* is an interrogative sentence—it asks something. A *negative statement* is a declarative sentence that somehow says, "No." A negative statement will probably contain an adverb like *not* or *never* modifying its verb.

In questions and negative statements, verb phrases are often split up, with the auxiliary verbs in one place and the main verb in another. Even though the words of the phrase are separated, they do the job of one verb, so they are still considered a verb phrase.

In questions, the subject usually separates the helping verb or verbs from the main verb. In the example below, the subject *Sally* separates the helping verb *did* from the main verb *understand*.

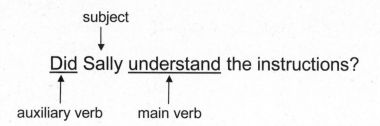

If we rewrite the question as a statement, we can put the verb phrase back together again—and give a possible answer for the question.

Sally <u>did understand</u> the instructions.

In negative statements, the negative word usually separates the helping verbs from the main verbs. In the example below, *never* separates the helping verb *would* from the main verb *be.*

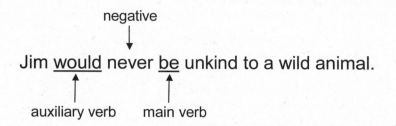

If we rewrite the negative statement as a positive, we can put the verb phrase back together again—but we do reverse the meaning of the sentence!

Jim <u>would be</u> unkind to a wild animal.

Name _____   Date _____

Try It

Write four sentences with divided verb phrases—two questions and two negative statements. Underline the auxiliary and main verbs. If you like, your negative statements can be the answers to your questions.

Example: <u>Are</u> we <u>getting</u> a new kitten this summer?
             No, we <u>are</u> not <u>getting</u> a new kitten this summer.

1. _____

2. _____

3. _____

4. _____

Name _____ Date _____

Try It

Let's review what you have learned about verbs. Answer the following questions.

Part A: Identifying Action Verbs and Being Verbs
Underline the verb in each sentence. Is it an action verb or a being verb? Circle the letter of the correct answer.

1. Jeff is a very good wrestler.
    a. action
    b. being

2. Our car shook on the bumpy gravel road.
    a. action
    b. being

3. Aunt Alice roasted peanuts from her garden.
    a. action
    b. being

Part B: Using Action Verbs
Complete each sentence with an action verb.

4. Terrance _____ the ball across the field.

5. The young children _____ when they saw the elephants.

Part C: Using Forms of *Be* and *Do* in Sentences
Circle the correct verb in parentheses.

6.   I (am, is) glad that Jake (is, are) in my karate class.

7.   The twins (is, are) on a soccer team this year, but they (was, were) on a softball team last year.

8.   (Does, Do) it make you angry when people (doesn't, don't) use good manners?

9.   I (was, were) certain that it would rain today, but now I (do, does) think it will be sunny.

10. My neighbor (don't, doesn't) want us to climb his fence.

Part D: Identifying Verb Phrases in Sentences
Underline the verb phrase in each sentence. Write on the lines the auxiliary verb(s) and the main verb.

	Auxiliary Verb	Main Verb
11. We will clean the garage Saturday.	_____	_____
12. I can swim ten laps at the pool.	_____	_____
13. It has been raining all weekend!	_____	_____
14. Norman could play the clarinet and tuba.	_____	_____
15. The duck's eggs have hatched.	_____	_____

Part E: Verb Phrases in Positive and Negative Statements
Underline the main verb and the auxiliary verb in each sentence.

16. The restaurant does not open until five o'clock.

17. Certain trees do lose their leaves each year.

18. The airplane will not land on time due to poor weather conditions.

Part F: Verb Phrases in Questions
Underline the main verb and auxiliary verb in each question.

19. Can you remember the words to that song?

20. Did you see the lunar eclipse last night?

Name _____ Date _____

Midterm Cumulative Review, Part 1

Today you're going to review what you've learned so far in Units 1, 2, and 3. Rewrite each sentence with correct punctuation and capitalization.

1. capt gunther is this flight going to paris france

   _____

   _____

2. russian and american space shuttles were launched on july 15 1975

   _____

   _____

3. the turkey uncle frank said smells delicious

   _____

   _____

4. maple syrup is produced in new york michigan and vermont

   _____

   _____

5. yes you may borrow my skates but please return them tomorrow

   _____

   _____

6. some people think a camels hump holds water but its really a mound of fat

_____

_____

7. watch out for that huge wave

_____

_____

8. i may go to the gym later or I may just jog around the neighborhood

_____

_____

Circle the answer that is written correctly.

9.   salutation of a letter
   a. Dear William,
   b. Dear William.

10. complimentary close of a letter
    a. Your friend.
    b. Your friend,

11. book title, written by hand
    a. <u>Treasure Island</u>
    b. "Treasure Island"

12. movie title, typed
    a. *The Wizard of Oz*
    b. <u>The Wizard of Oz</u>

13. song title
    a. <u>America, the Beautiful</u>
    b. "America, the Beautiful"

14. story title
    a. <u>How the Leopard Got Its Spots</u>
    b. "How the Leopard Got Its Spots"

15. poem title
    a. "The Midnight Ride of Paul Revere"
    b. <u>The Midnight Ride of Paul Revere</u>

16. TV show title
    a. <u>Jeopardy</u>
    b. "Jeopardy"

Complete each sentence with the kind of noun requested in parentheses.

17. _____ were arranged neatly on the grocery store shelf.
    (common noun, plural)

18. Please put your toys in the _____.
    (common noun, singular)

19. Daniel's tennis partner is _____.
    (proper noun, singular)

20. While she waited for the dentist, Fran read many _____.
    (common noun, plural)

Complete each sentence with the possessive form of the noun at the right.

21. A _____ legs can be up to six inches long.   (tarantula)

22. The park ranger searched for the _____ trail.   (campers)

23. I wanted to sit, but the _____ legs looked wobbly.   (chair)

24. A _____ crown is usually adorned with jewels.   (king)

25. We could not see beyond the _____ peak.   (mountain)

Change the italicized word(s) in each sentence to a pronoun. Write it on the line.

26. *Helen Cole* collects rocks and arrowheads.

    _____ collects rocks and arrowheads.

27. The winner of the photography contest is *Martin*.

    The winner of the photography contest is _____.

28. I accidentally kicked *Elizabeth* during our soccer game.

    I accidentally kicked _____ during our soccer game.

29. Please give your tickets to the *ushers*.

    Please give your tickets to _____.

30. *Jason and Maria* have braces on their teeth.

    _____ have braces on their teeth.

Name _____   Date _____

Midterm Cumulative Review, Part 2

Complete each sentence with the kind of pronoun requested in parentheses.

1. Our waiter brought _____ a basket of hot rolls and muffins.
   (first person, plural, object)

2. Do _____ know that a baby blue whale can drink 100 gallons
   of milk in a day?   (second person)

3. _____ was the first woman to win three Olympic gold medals.
   (third person, singular, subject)

4. In our science club _____ built an anemometer to measure wind.
   (first person, plural, subject)

5. David jumped, but the wasp stung _____ on his leg.
   (third person, singular, object)

6. We agreed among _____ that Chip would be the team captain.
   (reflexive pronoun)

7. The queen _____ entered the royal palace.
   (intensive pronoun)

On the line, write a possessive pronoun for the italicized words in each sentence.

8. I hope my poem will be chosen for the literary journal.

   I hope _____ will be chosen for the literary journal.

9. Kathy keeps her paintbrushes in a large jar.

   Kathy keeps _____ in a large jar.

10. Timothy called and said he left your bicycle helmet on the front porch.

    Timothy called and said he left _____ on the front porch.

Complete each sentence with the contraction for the words on the right.

11. If you don't hurry, _____ going to miss the bus!   (You are)

12. _____ like to have a surprise party for Mario.   (They would)

Complete each sentence with the word or kind of word requested in parentheses.

13. She arranged the roses in a _____ vase.
    (common adjective)

14. Ling Su's family always celebrates the _____ New Year.
    (proper adjective formed from China)

15. _____ glacier looked magnificent in the sunset.
    (definite article)

16. Kevin, the quarterback, twisted _____ ankle when he was tackled.
    (possessive adjective)

17. _____ octopus can shoot a stream of black ink at its attackers.
    (indefinite article)

18. _____ milk tastes sour.
    (demonstrative adjective, near)

19. Do you think you can swim to _____ side of the lake? (demonstrative adjective, far)

20. Josh planted a packet of seeds, but only _____ seeds sprouted. (adjective that tells how many)

21. The air feels _____ today than it did yesterday. (comparative adjective)

22. Rudy _____ his bicycle every Saturday morning. (action verb)

Circle the correct form of the verb to complete the sentence.

23. The thermometer on the porch _____ broken.
    a. am
    b. is

24. The factory had to close early because there _____ no electricity to operate the machines.
    a. was
    b. were

25. We learned that water _____ evaporate when it is boiled.
    a. do
    b. does

26. Palm trees _____ usually not grown in cold climates.
    a. is
    b. are

27. I _____ nervous about singing a solo in the concert.
    a. am
    b. is

Write sentences using verb phrases as requested. Underline the auxiliary and main verbs.

28. (positive statement)

_____

_____

29. (negative statement with a divided verb phrase)

_____

_____

30. (question with a divided verb phrase)

_____

_____

Name_____   Date_____

Get Ready

Verbs have four principal parts:
present, present participle, past, and past participle.

"Principal parts" means "most important pieces." You can make all the other forms of the verb from the principal parts.

The Four Principal Parts

1. Present

Present shows state of being or action happening now.

Fill in the blanks below with the present tense of *see* and *watch* (use each verb once).

1. I _____ movies every week.

2. I _____ them at the local movie theater.

2. Present Participle

The present participle of a verb is formed by adding *-ing* to the present. In a sentence, the present participle is used with a being verb as a helping verb.

Fill in the blanks below with the present participles of *see* and *watch* (use each verb once).

3. Tonight I am _____ an action film.

4. My father is _____ the movie with me.

3. Past

The past shows action or state of being in the past.

The past of *regular* verbs is formed by adding *-d or -ed* to the present.

The past of *irregular* verbs ends in something other than *-ed*.

Fill in the blanks with the past of *see* and *watch* (use each verb once).

5. I _____ *The Sound of Music* when I was seven.

6. I _____ it about ten times!

4. Past Participle

The past participle shows action or state of being in the past.

The past participle of regular verbs is formed by adding *-d* or *-ed* to the present. The past participle of irregular verbs ends in something else. In a sentence, the past participle is used with the helping verb *has, have*, or *had*.

Fill in the blanks below with the past participle of *see* and *watch.* (Use each verb once.)

7. I have _____ hundreds of movies in my life.

8. I have _____ them with my family, my friends, and by myself.

Now that you have used *see* and *watch* in sentences and know how to recognize an irregular verb, which one is irregular?

_____

To prepare for the workbook exercises, study this list of irregular verbs. Some may be familiar, but others may be new to you. Practice reciting the principal parts.

Some Irregular Verbs

Present	Present Participle	Past	Past Participle
come	coming	came	come
do	doing	did	done
fall	falling	fell	fallen
go	going	went	gone
grow	growing	grew	grown
hurt	hurting	hurt	hurt
know	knowing	knew	known
lay	laying	laid	laid
make	making	made	made
rise	rising	rose	risen
see	seeing	saw	seen
sink	sinking	sank	sunk
stand	standing	stood	stood
take	taking	took	taken
teach	teaching	taught	taught
write	writing	wrote	written

Name _____ Date _____

Get Ready

Regular and irregular English verbs have four principal parts:

- present
- present participle (uses helping verbs *is, am, are, was, were*)
- past
- past participle (uses helping verbs *has, have, had*)

You know that *-ed* is the ending for the past and the past participle forms of regular verbs: *turned, released, snowboarded, tumbled.*

The past and past participle forms of an *irregular* verb do <u>not</u> end in *-ed*. Since irregular verbs are unpredictable, you must practice and learn them. Here are a few more irregular verbs for you to study:

Some Irregular Verbs

Present	Present Participle	Past	Past Participle
be (am/is/are)	being	was/were	been
build	building	built	built
eat	eating	ate	eaten
find	finding	found	found
leave	leaving	left	left

Name _____   Date _____

Get Ready

Can you name the four principal parts of verbs?

- present
- present participle (uses helping verbs *is, am, are, was, were*)
- past
- past participle (uses helping verbs *has, have, had*)

Do you remember how to form the past and past participle of a regular verb?

You add *-d* or *-ed* to the present form of the verb. For example, *move* becomes *move**d***, and *dream* becomes *dream**ed***.

However, you just have to memorize the past and past participle forms of irregular verbs because—well, because they're not regular!

Study the principal parts of the irregular verbs *break, see, go,* and *choose*.

Present	Present Participle	Past	Past Participle
break	breaking	broke	broken
see	seeing	saw	seen
go	going	went	gone
choose	choosing	chose	chosen

Name _____   Date _____

Get Ready

Verbs in English have four principal parts:
- present
- present participle (uses helping verbs *is, am, are, was, were*)
- past
- past participle (uses helping verbs *has, have, had*)

You form the past and past participle of a *regular verb* by adding -*d* or -*ed*. The past and past participle forms of *irregular verbs*, however, are unpredictable.

Study the principal parts of the irregular verb *take*.

Present	Present Participle	Past	Past Participle
take	taking	took	taken

Exercises in English will give you more practice using *take*.

Name _____   Date _____

Try It: Sentence Analysis

Analyze these sentences. Ask for help if you need it.

Sentence Analysis Questions
1. Sentence or fragment?
2. Kind of sentence?
3. Verb?
4. Simple subject?
5. Direct object or subject complement?
6. Modifiers?
7. Parts of speech?

1. Ali tiptoed nervously to the door of his sick father's room.

Sentence or fragment?   _____

Kind of sentence?   _____

Verb?   _____

Simple subject?   _____

Direct object or
subject complement?   _____

Modifiers?   _____

Parts of speech?   Ali   _____   of   _____
                      tiptoed _____   his   _____
                      nervously _____   sick   _____
                      to   _____   father's _____
                      the   _____   room   _____
                      door   _____

2. Strangely, every bone in Ali's body was obeying the dirty old beggar!

Sentence or fragment? _____

Kind of sentence? _____

Verb? _____

Simple subject? _____

Direct object or
subject complement? _____

Modifiers? _____

Parts of speech? Strangely _____ was obeying _____

every _____ the _____

bone _____ dirty _____

in _____ old _____

Ali's _____ beggar _____

body _____

3. You will be a source of pride and joy to your parents now and forever.

Sentence or fragment? _____

Kind of sentence? _____

Verb? _____

Simple subject? _____

Direct object or
subject complement? _____

Modifiers? _____

Parts of speech?

You	_____	joy	_____
will be	_____	to	_____
a	_____	your	_____
source	_____	parents	_____
of	_____	now	_____
pride	_____	and	_____
and	_____	forever	_____

Name _____ Date _____

Get Ready

You know that verbs express action or state of being. A verb also tells *when* something happens—in the present, the past, or the future. The time of a verb is called its *tense*.

Past tense verbs show action or state of being that happened in the past, or previously.

Which verbs below show past time? Underline them.

will cut	am hiding	wandered
drove	had seen	took
chooses	have broken	will be
identified	fold	has been

Regular verbs will end in *-ed* in the simple past tense, and irregular verbs will have unpredictable endings. For example,

I <u>studied</u> my lines hard and <u>knew</u> them well.
(*studied* is regular and *knew* is irregular)

Other past tenses are formed by adding *have, has,* or *had* as a helping verb to a *past participle*. Again, regular verbs will end in *-ed* in these forms, and irregular verbs will have unpredictable endings. For example,

We <u>have put</u> on an excellent play. (irregular)
The director <u>has been</u> very patient with us. (irregular)
Until now, we <u>had performed</u> only at home! (regular)

Practice using the past tense in *Exercises in English*.

144

Name _____   Date _____

Try It: Diagramming Sentences

Sentence Diagramming Steps

1. Verb?
Write the verb on the main diagram line.

2. Subject?
Write the subject in front of the verb on the main diagram line. Draw a short vertical line (that cuts through the main line) to separate the subject and the verb.

3. Direct object or subject complement, if any?
Write the direct object or subject complement after the verb on the main diagram line, with a short vertical (for direct object) or slanted (for subject complement) line between them.

4. Verb modifiers, if any?
Write the modifiers on slanted lines below the verb.

5. Subject modifiers, if any?
Write the modifiers on slanted lines below the subject.

6. Direct object or subject complement modifiers, if any?
Write the modifiers on slanted lines below the direct object or subject complement.

Diagram these three sentences. Ask for help if you need it.

1. Ali ibn Ali was spoiled and selfish.

2. My ill father is whispering strange words.

3. Ali soon bought the precious healing ingredients.

Name _____ Date _____

Get Ready

Verb Tense

Verb tense shows the time of the action or state of being described in the verb. Verb tenses can show present, past, or future time.

1. present
- "This <u>is</u> a terrible movie," moaned Bill
- "I <u>am dying</u> of boredom," agreed Tim.

2. past
- "Last night, we <u>were falling</u> asleep at the movies," said Bill.
- "We <u>snored</u> more than we <u>watched</u>!" exclaimed Tim.

3. future
- The boys declared, "We <u>will go</u> to a different movie tonight."

Simple Tenses

There are three simple tenses: *simple present, simple past,* and *simple future*.

1. simple present
The simple present tells about something that

- happens now: Ben *bakes* blueberry muffins.
- happens again and again: City workers *clean* the parks.
- is always true: The Earth *circles* the sun.

2. simple past
In the simple past, regular verbs will end in *-ed*, and irregular verbs will have unpredictable endings. The simple past tells about something that happened in the past.

- My family *visited* Yosemite National Park in 2001.

3. simple future

The simple future combines the helping verbs *shall* or *will* with the *present* of the verb. The simple future tells about something that will happen in the future.

- We <u>will hike</u> in Zion National Park next summer.

Progressive Tenses

There are two progressive tenses: *present progressive* and *past progressive*.

1. present progressive

The present progressive combines a *present tense form of be* (*am*, *is*, or *are*) with the *present participle* of a verb. The present progressive tense tells about something happening right now.

- Harry <u>is feeling</u> ill today.

2. past progressive

The *past progressive* combines a *past tense form of be* (*was* or *were*) with the *present participle* of a verb. The past progressive tense tells about something that was in progress sometime in the past.

- I <u>was thinking</u> that he <u>wasn't looking</u> so good!

Name Date

Perfect Tenses

The tense of a verb shows when something happened. In addition to the three simple tenses, verbs have three *perfect* tenses.

Tense	Example (singular subject)	Example (plural subject)
present	Kelsey **loves** her hat.	We **tell** the story.
past	Kelsey **loved** her hat.	We **told** the story.
future	Kelsey **will love** her hat.	We **will tell** the story.
present perfect	Kelsey **has loved** her hat.	We **have told** the story.
past perfect	Kelsey **had loved** her hat.	We **had told** the story.
future perfect	Kelsey **will have loved** her hat.	We **will have told** the story.

Present Perfect Tense

A verb in the **present perfect tense** shows action that happened at a vague time in the past. A verb in the present perfect tense can also show action that started in the past and has continued into the present.

To form the present perfect tense, use *have* or *has* before a verb's past participle.

> They **have eaten** at this restaurant. (They ate at the restaurant sometime in the past, but it's not clear when.)

She **has ordered** spaghetti and chocolate milk since we were children.
(She ordered that meal in the past, and she still orders it.)

Past Perfect Tense

A verb in the **past perfect tense** shows action that was completed in the past before another action happened.

To form the past perfect tense, use *had* before a verb's past participle.

We **had cleaned** the entire house before the guests arrived. (The action was completed before the guests arrived.)

Future Perfect Tense

A verb in the **future perfect tense** shows action that will be completed in the future before another action happens.

To form the future perfect tense, use *will have* before a verb's past participle.

I **will have moved** into a new apartment by this time next week. (The action will be completed before this time next week.)

Write the given verb in the given tense to complete the sentence.

1. We _____ in this neighborhood for twenty years. (Verb: live; Tense: present perfect)

2. The florist _____ the flowers before the wedding begins. (Verb: deliver; Tense: future perfect)

3. Mario _____ vanilla ice cream before he knew there was also chocolate. (Verb: choose; Tense: past perfect)

Identify the verb tense of the underlined verb in each sentence. Explain the difference in the meaning of the sentences.

4. Tanya <u>has gone</u> to this farmer's market for months. _____

Tanya <u>went</u> to this farmer's market for weeks. _____

_____

_____

_____

_____

5. The twins <u>have worn</u> only the color purple for years. _____

The twins <u>had worn</u> only the color purple for years. _____

_____

_____

_____

_____

6. Rodney <u>will have washed</u> the dishes before Mom asks. _____

Rodney <u>will wash</u> the dishes before Mom asks. _____

_____

_____

_____

_____

Write a sentence that uses a verb in the given tense.

7. present perfect

_____

_____

_____

8. past perfect

_____

_____

_____

9. future perfect

_____

_____

_____

Name _____ Date _____

Get Ready

What do you remember about direct objects? Can you answer these questions?

What kind of verb does a direct object follow?
What part of speech is a direct object?
What does a direct object do in a sentence?
How do you find a direct object in a sentence?

A direct object is a noun or pronoun that receives the action of an action verb.

Transitive Verbs

The verb in a sentence with a direct object is called a *transitive verb*. The word *transitive,* which comes from Latin, means "going across." How does "going across" relate to verbs? Read these examples.

1. The dog bites the man.
2. The man bites the dog.

In the first sentence, who *does* the action—that is, who bites? Who *receives* the action—that is, who is bitten?

In the second sentence, who does the action? Who receives the action?

The two sentences show how transitive verbs work. The action of a transitive verb goes across—or passes—*from* the doer (the subject) *to* the receiver (direct object).

As you can see, who does and who receives the action makes a big difference in the meaning of the sentence!

Name _____ Date _____

Shifts in Verb Tense

In general, the verbs in a sentence should be in the same tense. These sentences use verb tense correctly.

> CORRECT: They **ran** to the park and **swung** on the swings. (Both verbs are in the past tense.)

> CORRECT: I **am blinking** and **hopping** on one foot at the same time. (Both verbs are in the present progressive tense.)

> CORRECT: Yvette **had locked** the door before she **went** outside. (The tense shifts correctly from past perfect to past because one action occurred before the other.)

When the verbs in a sentence have different tenses, that is called a **shift in tense**. To correct an inappropriate shift in tense, pick a single tense and use it throughout the sentence.

> INCORRECT: Jack **sleeps** in a tent and **dreamed** about crickets. (*Sleeps* is in the present tense, but *dreamed* is in the past tense.)

> CORRECT: Jack **sleeps** in a tent and **dreams** about crickets. (Both verbs are in the present tense.)

> CORRECT: Jack **slept** in a tent and **dreamed** about crickets. (Both verbs are in the past tense.)

State whether the sentence has an inappropriate shift in tense. If yes, rewrite the sentence to correct the shift in tense.

1. Gianna runs through the sprinkler and got wet. _____

_____

_____

2. Liam sang and juggled in the community talent show. _____

_____

_____

3. Jeremiah washes and dried the silverware after dinner. _____

_____

_____

4. In February, Myndi will visit California and saw the giant redwoods. _____

_____

_____

5. At the top of the tree, a bird sits in her nest and protects her babies. _____

_____

_____

6. Tony raises his hand and asked a question. _____

_____

_____

Name _____   Date _____

Try It

True or False? Write T or F on the line.

____ 1. A direct object can complete the meaning of an action verb.

____ 2. Only sentences with action verbs can have direct objects.

____ 3. Not all sentences with action verbs have direct objects.

____ 4. The action verb in a sentence with a direct object is transitive.

____ 5. The subject of a transitive verb is the receiver of the action.

____ 6. The direct object of a transitive verb is the doer of the action.

Name _____ Date _____

Get Ready

Which sentences below have transitive verbs? How do you know?

1. Sandy ate all the candy in the bag.
2. Then Sandy gobbled an entire pizza.
3. After that, Sandy stopped.
4. Finally, Sandy was full.

Intransitive Verbs

You know that a verb that has a direct object is called *transitive*. Transitive verbs pass action across from a doer to a receiver.

But what about sentences without a direct object? The verb in a sentence without a direct object is called an *intransitive verb*. Intransitive means "not going across."

A sentence with an intransitive verb has a subject, or doer; but it doesn't have a direct object, or receiver. Why not? The sentence may

- not name any direct object
  example: Fernando was reading.

- not need a direct object to make sense
  example: Grandpa yelled.

- not have an action for a direct object to receive, because the sentence has a linking verb
  example: Mrs. Sanger is tired.

Look at the sentences at the top of the page again. The verbs in the third and fourth sentences are intransitive. In the third sentence *stopped* is an action verb, but no direct object is named, so no action passes from doer to receiver. Besides, the sentence makes sense as it is.

In the fourth sentence *was* is a linking verb, so *full* is a subject complement that describes the subject—not a direct object that receives action.

Name _____ **Date** _____

Try It

Find and underline the six intransitive verbs in the following passage.

There are three main kinds of rock. Sedimentary rock forms from layers of sand, mud, and seashells. Great heat and pressure create metamorphic rock. Igneous rock comes from rock that has melted and then cooled.

Rock has many purposes. Building designers use granite. Sculptors often carve marble for statues. Stonemasons work with rocks all the time. They build walls, chimneys, and foundations, among other things.

Name _____   **Date** _____

Get Ready

What Am I?
Fill in the blank with a term from the Answer Bank that names what is described in the sentence.

Answer Bank

intransitive verb
transitive verb
direct object
subject
linking verb
action verb

1. I pass action from a doer to a receiver. What am I?

   _____

2. I am the doer of the action in a sentence. What am I?

   _____

3. I am the receiver of the action in a sentence. What am I?

   _____

4. I am a verb that is never transitive. What am I?

   _____

5. I never have a direct object. What am I?

   _____

6. Sometimes I have a direct object, and sometimes I don't. What am I?

   _____

Name _____   Date _____

Try It: Analyzing and Diagramming Sentences

Sentence Analysis Questions

1. Sentence or fragment?
2. Kind of sentence?
3. Verb?
4. Simple subject?
5. Direct object or subject complement?
6. Modifiers?
7. Parts of speech?

Sentence Diagramming Steps

1. Verb?
Write the verb on the main diagram line.

2. Subject?
Write the subject in front of the verb on the main diagram line. Draw a short vertical line (that cuts through the main line) to separate the subject and the verb.

3. Direct object or subject complement, if any?
Write the direct object or subject complement after the verb on the main diagram line. Draw a short vertical (for direct object) or slanted (for subject complement) line between them.

4. Verb modifiers, if any?
Write the modifiers on slanted lines below the verb.

5. Subject modifiers, if any?
Write the modifiers on slanted lines below the subject.

6. Direct object or subject complement modifiers, if any?
Write the modifiers on slanted lines below the direct object or subject complement.

Analyze and diagram the following sentences. Ask for help if you need it.

1. The striped top was humming and was spinning crazily.

Sentence or fragment? _____

Kind of sentence? _____

Verb? _____

Simple subject? _____

Direct object or
subject complement? _____

Modifiers? _____

Parts of speech?
The   _____   and   _____
striped   _____   was spinning _____
top   _____   crazily   _____
was humming _____

Diagram:

2. Soon, the busy little toy will fall sideways.

Sentence or fragment? _____

Kind of sentence? _____

Verb? _____

Simple subject? _____

Direct object or
subject complement? _____

Modifiers? _____

Parts of speech?

Soon	_____	toy	_____
the	_____	will fall	_____
busy	_____	sideways	_____
little	_____		

Diagram:

Name   Date

Perfect Tenses

The tense of a verb shows when something happened. In addition to the three simple tenses, verbs have three *perfect* tenses.

Tense	Example (singular subject)	Example (plural subject)
present	Kelsey **loves** her hat.	We **tell** the story.
past	Kelsey **loved** her hat.	We **told** the story.
future	Kelsey **will love** her hat.	We **will tell** the story.
present perfect	Kelsey **has loved** her hat.	We **have told** the story.
past perfect	Kelsey **had loved** her hat.	We **had told** the story.
future perfect	Kelsey **will have loved** her hat.	We **will have told** the story.

Present Perfect Tense

A verb in the **present perfect tense** shows action that happened at a vague time in the past. A verb in the present perfect tense can also show action that started in the past and has continued into the present.

To form the present perfect tense, use *have* or *has* before a verb's past participle.

> They **have eaten** at this restaurant. (They ate at the restaurant sometime in the past, but it's not clear when.)

She **has ordered** spaghetti and chocolate milk since we were children.
(She ordered that meal in the past, and she still orders it.)

Past Perfect Tense

A verb in the **past perfect tense** shows action that was completed in the past before another action happened.

To form the past perfect tense, use *had* before a verb's past participle.

We **had cleaned** the entire house before the guests arrived. (The action was completed before the guests arrived.)

Future Perfect Tense

A verb in the **future perfect tense** shows action that will be completed in the future before another action happens.

To form the future perfect tense, use *will have* before a verb's past participle.

I **will have moved** into a new apartment by this time next week. (The action will be completed before this time next week.)

Write the given verb in the given tense to complete the sentence.

1. We _____ in this neighborhood for twenty years. (Verb: live; Tense: present perfect)

2. The florist _____ the flowers before the wedding begins. (Verb: deliver; Tense: future perfect)

3. Mario _____ vanilla ice cream before he knew there was also chocolate. (Verb: choose; Tense: past perfect)

Identify the verb tense of the underlined verb in each sentence. Explain the difference in the meaning of the sentences.

4. Tanya <u>has gone</u> to this farmer's market for months. _____

Tanya <u>went</u> to this farmer's market for weeks. _____

_____

_____

_____

_____

5. The twins <u>have worn</u> only the color purple for years. _____

The twins <u>had worn</u> only the color purple for years. _____

_____

_____

_____

_____

6. Rodney <u>will have washed</u> the dishes before Mom asks. _____

Rodney <u>will wash</u> the dishes before Mom asks. _____

_____

_____

_____

_____

Write a sentence that uses a verb in the given tense.

7. present perfect

_____

_____

_____

8. past perfect

_____

_____

_____

9. future perfect

_____

_____

_____

Name   Date

Shifts in Verb Tense

In general, the verbs in a sentence should be in the same tense. These sentences use verb tense correctly.

> CORRECT: They **ran** to the park and **swung** on the swings. (Both verbs are in the past tense.)

> CORRECT: I **am blinking** and **hopping** on one foot at the same time. (Both verbs are in the present progressive tense.)

> CORRECT: Yvette **had locked** the door before she **went** outside. (The tense shifts correctly from past perfect to past because one action occurred before the other.)

When the verbs in a sentence have different tenses, that is called a **shift in tense**. To correct an inappropriate shift in tense, pick a single tense and use it throughout the sentence.

> INCORRECT: Jack **sleeps** in a tent and **dreamed** about crickets. (*Sleeps* is in the present tense, but *dreamed* is in the past tense.)

> CORRECT: Jack **sleeps** in a tent and **dreams** about crickets. (Both verbs are in the present tense.)

> CORRECT: Jack **slept** in a tent and **dreamed** about crickets. (Both verbs are in the past tense.)

State whether the sentence has an inappropriate shift in tense. If yes, rewrite the sentence to correct the shift in tense.

1. Gianna runs through the sprinkler and got wet. _____

_____

_____

2. Liam sang and juggled in the community talent show. _____

_____

_____

3. Jeremiah washes and dried the silverware after dinner. _____

_____

_____

4. In February, Myndi will visit California and saw the giant redwoods. _____

_____

_____

5. At the top of the tree, a bird sits in her nest and protects her babies. _____

_____

_____

6. Tony raises his hand and asked a question. _____

_____

_____

Name _____   Date _____

Try It

Let's review what you have learned about verbs. Answer the following questions.

Part 1: Principal Parts of Verbs

Write the present participle, the past, and the past participle of each verb.

	Present Participle	**Past**	**Past Participle**
Example: fall	falling	fell	fallen
1. write	_____	_____	_____
2. make	_____	_____	_____
3. do	_____	_____	_____
4. rise	_____	_____	_____
5. hop	_____	_____	_____

Part 2: Regular and Irregular Verbs

The verb or verb phrase is underlined in each sentence. Write **R** on the line if the principal verb is **regular** or **I** if it is **irregular**.

Example: I_____This stone castle <u>was built</u> in 1780.

6. _____ Jack <u>knew</u> the answers to all of the difficult questions.

7. _____ My sister <u>talks</u> on the telephone for hours every night.

8. _____ The dough for the cinnamon rolls <u>has risen</u> in the pan.

Part 3: Past and Past Participle Forms of Verbs

Complete each sentence with the simple past or the past participle of the verb.

Example: Uncle Frank <u>taught</u> us how to play croquet. (teach)

9. We_____the tools we needed in the garage.   (find)

10. My friends had_____the players for the game before I got to the park. (pick)

11. Mike had_____four inches since his grandparents' last visit. (grow)

12. The golden retriever_____through several hoops during the dog show. (jump)

Part 4: Using Irregular Verbs in Sentences

Complete each sentence with the correct form of the verb in parentheses.

Example: We <u>saw</u> this movie last month. (see)

13. The children have_____all of the crayons in the box. (break)

14. Have you ever_____a shooting star in the sky? (see)

15. Yesterday we_____to the Grand Canyon. (go)

16. Kevin hasn't_____a name yet for his new pet turtle.   (choose)

17. Our friends_____us fishing on the lake last weekend.   (take)

Part 5: Verb Tenses
Complete each sentence with the verb requested in parentheses.

Example: Adam <u>lives</u> near the skating rink. (simple present tense, *live*)

18. I_____a cold after playing outside in the snow all afternoon.
     (simple past tense, *catch*)

19. Ray's father_____a helicopter for a sight-seeing company in
     Alaska. (simple present tense, *fly*)

20. Who do you think_____the Super Bowl this year?
     (simple future tense, *win*)

21. I certainly_____this new book by my favorite author.
     (present progressive tense, *enjoy*)

22. They_____in the airport for their aunt's plane to arrive.
     (past progressive tense, *wait*)

Part 6: Identifying Transitive and Intransitive Verbs
Write **T** on the line if the italicized verb is **transitive**. Write **I** if it is **intransitive**.

Example: **T**___I *collected* five pounds of cans during our recycling project.

23. ____ Luke *scraped* his knee when he tried to climb over the fence.

24. ____ The fans *cheered* loudly when the rock star appeared on the stage.

25. ____ We *crawled* into our sleeping bags and began telling scary stories
         around the campfire.

26. ___ Floodwaters *destroyed* many homes along the banks of the river.

Part 7: Using Transitive and Intransitive Verbs in Sentences

Write sentences using each verb as requested.

(Answers will vary.)

Example: (*carried* as a transitive verb)
<u>The Indians carried baskets of corn on their heads.</u>

27. (*pulled* as a transitive verb)

_____

28. (*sing* as an intransitive verb)

_____

29. (*flew* as an intransitive verb)

_____

30. (*found* as a transitive verb)

_____

Name _____   Date _____

Get Ready

Linking verbs link or connect instead of showing action. The most common linking verbs are forms of *be:*

am	is	are	was	were
am being	is being	are being	was being	were being
will be	shall be	have been	has been	had been

A linking verb connects the subject to a noun, pronoun, or adjective after the verb—that is, a subject complement. The subject complement tells more about, or somehow defines the subject.

In the sentences below, the linking verb is underlined, and the subject and subject complement are italicized. Decide whether the subject complement is a noun, pronoun, or adjective.

1. This *book* <u>was</u> *interesting*.   _____

2. The team *captain* <u>is</u> *he*.   _____

3. *We* <u>will be</u> *stagehands* for the play.   _____

A linking verb acts like an equal sign, showing how the subject and its complement balance and complete each other.

The largest mammal is the blue whale.
largest mammal = blue whale

Name _____   **Date** _____

Try It

Write six sentences with linking verbs from the Word Bank. Two of the subject complements should be nouns, two should be pronouns, and two should be adjectives. Circle and label the part of speech of each subject complement.

Word Bank

am	is	are	was	were
am being	is being	are being	was being	were being
will be	shall be	have been	has been	had been

1. _____

_____

2. _____

_____

3. _____

_____

4. _____

_____

5. _____

_____

6. _____

_____

Name _____   Date _____

Get Ready

Subjects and verbs are partners and must *agree* in *number*. A singular subject must team up with a singular verb, and a plural subject must team up with a plural verb.

Subjects and verbs must also agree in *person*. A verb may have different forms for first, second, and third person subjects.

Do you remember how to tell whether a noun or pronoun is singular, plural, or first, second, or third person?

Look at this list and answer the questions below:

| keys | truck | we | glasses | you |
| oxen | I | nail | he | they |

1. Which of the nouns and pronouns are singular? Which are plural? How do you know?
2. Which pronouns are first person? Why?
3. Which pronoun is second person? Why?
4. Which of the nouns and pronouns are third person? Why?

How can verbs reflect number and person? The charts on the next page show how singular and plural forms of the verbs *be, wait,* and *do* agree in number and person with the personal pronouns and also with nouns, which are third person subjects.

Simple Present Forms of *Be*

Singular	Plural
I am	we are
you are	you are
he is, she is, it is	they are
Janet is, pencil is	books are, people are

Simple Present Forms of *Wait*

Singular	Plural
I *wait*	we *wait*
you *wait*	you *wait*
he *waits*, she *waits*, it *waits*	they *wait*
Fifi *waits*, boy *waits*	cows *wait*, men *wait*

Simple Present Forms of *Do*

Singular	Plural
I *do*	we *do*
you *do*	you *do*
he *does*, she *does*, it *does*	they *do*
paint *does*, Jed *does*	cars *do*, bugs *do*

What patterns do you see?

Exercises in English will give you more practice with subject-verb agreement.

Name _____   Date _____

Try It: Sentence Analysis

Analyze the following two sentences. Ask for help if you need it.

Sentence Analysis Questions
1. Sentence or fragment?
2. Kind of sentence?
3. Verb?
4. Simple subject?
5. Direct object or subject complement?
6. Modifiers?
7. Parts of speech?

1. From an early age, Phillis Wheatley was a talented poet.

Sentence or fragment? _____

Kind of sentence? _____

Verb? _____

Simple subject? _____

Direct object or
subject complement? _____

Modifiers? _____

Parts of speech?

From	_____	was	_____
an	_____	a	_____
early	_____	talented	_____
age	_____	poet	_____
Phillis Wheatley	_____		

2. Hers was the first published book of English poetry by an African-American writer.

Sentence or fragment?   _____

Kind of sentence?   _____

Verb?   _____

Simple subject?   _____

Direct object or
subject complement?   _____

Modifiers?   _____

Parts of speech?

Hers	_____	English	_____
was	_____	poetry	_____
the	_____	by	_____
first	_____	an	_____
published	_____	African-American	_____
book	_____	writer	_____
of	_____		

Name _____ Date _____

Get Ready

Some words are easy to confuse because they sound exactly the same: *write* and *right*, for example, or *to*, *two*, and *too*.

Other words get mixed up because they sound similar, or because they are closely related. Let's study two verb pairs that get confused sometimes: *let* and *leave,* and *teach* and *learn*.

Let and Leave

Let usually means *permit* or *allow*.

<u>Let</u> me help you with that heavy bag of groceries.
My parents <u>aren't letting</u> any of us play outside today.
I <u>have let</u> you borrow my bike for long enough.

Practice saying the principal parts of *let* aloud. They are

present	let
present participle	letting
past	let
past participle	let

Leave usually means *depart* or *go without taking*.

She <u>left</u> her sweatshirt on the beach last week.
Don't <u>leave</u> without saying goodbye to everyone!
<u>Had</u> you <u>left</u> home before it started to rain?

Practice saying the principal parts of *leave* aloud. They are

present	leave
present participle	leaving
past	left
past participle	left

Teach and Learn

Teach means *instruct, educate,* or *pass on knowledge.*

Dad <u>is teaching</u> Mr. Austin how to fish from the dock.
Mom <u>has taught</u> art classes for ten years.
<u>Will</u> somebody <u>teach</u> me how to open this door?

Practice saying the principal parts of *teach* aloud. They are

present	teach
present participle	teaching
past	taught
past participle	taught

Learn means *be instructed, come to know,* or *acquire knowledge.*

Mr. Austin <u>is learning</u> how to fish from the dock.
Hundreds of students <u>have learned</u> about art in Mom's classes.
I want to <u>learn</u> how to open this door!

Practice saying the principal parts of *learn* aloud. They are

present	learn
present participle	learning
past	learned
past participle	learned

<u>Name</u>   <u>Date</u>

Get Ready

Some words are easy to confuse because they sound exactly the same: *hear* and *here*, for example. It is even more confusing when different verbs have some of the same principal parts!

Let's study one of the most frequently confused and misused verb pairs in the English language: *lie* and *lay*.

Lie and *Lay*

Lie usually means *recline, rest,* or *be in a horizontal position*. In the sentences below, notice that *lie* is intransitive—that is, the sentences don't have a direct object to receive the action.

<u>Lie</u> down and let me take your temperature.
The baby <u>was lying</u> in her cozy little bed.
When she had chicken pox, Susie <u>lay</u> on the couch all day.
We <u>have lain</u> in the yard at night and watched the stars.

Practice saying the principal parts of *lie* aloud. They are

present	lie
present participle	lying
past	lay
past participle	lain

Lay usually means *to put* or *place.* In the sentences below notice that *lay* is transitive—that is, the sentences have a direct object that receives the action of the verb.

Please <u>lay</u> the fork to the left of the plate.
Bobby <u>is laying</u> out the game so we can play.
I <u>laid</u> my pencil down when the test was over.
<u>Had</u> your chicken ever <u>laid</u> eggs before?

Practice saying the principal parts of *lay* aloud. They are

present	lay
present participle	laying
past	laid
past participle	laid

Name _____   Date _____

Try It

Read the following sentences. Are the underlined forms of *lie* and *lay* used correctly? If a verb is used incorrectly, write the correct form of the word on the blank line.

Hint: Remember that *lie* is an intransitive verb and *lay* is a transitive verb.

Example: You've worked hard. <u>Lay</u> down and relax!

    a. Is the verb used correctly?   Yes /(No)

    b. If no, correct the verb: lie _____

1.   When I was done raking, I <u>laid</u> down my rake.

    a. Is the verb used correctly?   Yes / No

    b. If no, correct the verb: _____

2.   Then my rake <u>lay</u> in a pile of leaves.

    a. Is the verb used correctly?   Yes / No

    b. If no, correct the verb: _____

3.   I have <u>laid</u> in bed all day today.

    a. Is the verb used correctly?   Yes / No

    b. If no, correct the verb: _____

4.   <u>Lay</u> your hat on the table there.

    a. Is the verb used correctly?   Yes / No

    b. If no, correct the verb: _____

5. <u>Lay</u> still on your cots for rest time, children!

      a. Is the verb used correctly?   Yes / No

      b. If no, correct the verb: _____

6. So that we wouldn't spoil the surprise, we <u>had lain</u> the presents out very quietly.

      a. Is the verb used correctly?   Yes / No

      b. If no, correct the verb: _____

7. Uncle Jim <u>is laying</u> on the lounge chair in the back yard.

      a. Is the verb used correctly?   Yes / No

      b. If no, correct the verb: _____

8. My brothers <u>were laying</u> out booby traps for us.

      a. Is the verb used correctly?   Yes / No

      b. If no, correct the verb: _____

9. <u>Lay</u> the necklace to hang like this on your collar.

      a. Is the verb used correctly?   Yes / No

      b. If no, correct the verb: _____

10. The wet hat <u>lay</u> in the puddle where someone had dropped it.

      a. Is the verb used correctly?   Yes / No

      b. If no, correct the verb: _____

Name _____   Date _____

Get Ready

Some words are easy to mix up because they sound exactly the same: *there* and *their*, for example. Other words get jumbled up because they sound similar. Let's study one more confusing verb pair: *sit* and *set.*

Sit and Set

Sit usually means *have a seat* or *have a place.* In the sentences below, notice that *sit* is intransitive—the sentences don't have direct objects.

> Dexter, please <u>sit</u> still on the bench.
> Where in the theater <u>are</u> you <u>sitting</u>?
> When I was little, my big sister <u>sat</u> on me a lot.
> Goldilocks <u>has sat</u> in every chair in the room.

Practice saying the principal parts of *sit* aloud. They are

present	sit
present participle	sitting
past	sat
past participle	sat

Set usually means *place* or *put in proper position*. In the sentences below, notice that *set* is transitive—the sentences have direct objects that name the objects that have been placed in position.

> Dr. Robic <u>will set</u> Billy's broken bone so that it heals properly.
> The farmers <u>are setting</u> out baby corn plants in rows.
> After shopping, Mom <u>set</u> the grocery bags on the counter.
> We <u>have set</u> the VCR to record the movie.

Practice saying the principal parts of *set* aloud. They are

present	set
present participle	setting
past	set
past participle	set

Exercises in English will give you more practice using *sit* and *set.*

Name _____   Date _____

Try It: Sentence Diagramming

Diagram these three sentences. Ask for help if you need it.

Sentence Diagramming Steps

1. **Verb?**
   Write the verb on the main diagram line.

2. **Subject?**
   Write the subject in front of the verb on the main diagram line. Draw a short vertical line (that cuts through the main line) to separate the subject and the verb.

3. **Direct object or subject complement, if any?**
   Write the direct object or subject complement after the verb on the main diagram line. Draw a short vertical (for direct object) or slanted (for subject complement) line between them.

4. **Verb modifiers, if any?**
   Write the modifiers on slanted lines below the verb.

5. **Subject modifiers, if any?**
   Write the modifiers on slanted lines below the subject.

6. **Direct object or subject complement modifiers, if any?**
   Write the modifiers on slanted lines below the direct object or subject complement.

Diagram these three sentences. Ask for help if you need it.

1. Brazil nuts are evergreen tree seeds.

2. This Brazilian evergreen tree flowers and produces a fleshy fruit.

3. The thick-walled fruit contains seeds, or nuts, inside.

Name _____   Date _____

Get Ready

What Am I?

Fill in the blanks below with a term from the Answer Bank. You will use some answers more than once.

Answer Bank

linking verb	learn
subject complement	sit
number	set
person	lay
let	lie
leave	lain
teach	laid

1. I mean "allow" or "permit." What am I? _____

2. I am the past participle of *lie*. What am I? _____

3. I mean "give knowledge." What am I? _____

4. I am the past of *lie* and the present of *lay*. What am I? _____

5. I mean "place" or "fix in proper position." What am I? _____

6. I mean "put" or "place." What am I? _____

7. I am often a being verb, and I act like an equal sign between a subject and its complement. What am I? _____

8. I mean "recline" or "rest." What am I? _____

9. I mean "depart" or "go without taking." What am I? _____

10. I do not show action. What am I? _____

11. I am a noun, pronoun, or adjective that refers to the subject and describes it. What am I? _____

12. We are two ways that subjects and verbs must agree. What are we? _____and _____

13. I mean "keep a seat." What am I? _____

14. I am the past participle of *lay*. What am I? _____

15. I mean "acquire knowledge." What am I? _____

Name _____   Date _____

Unit 9 Pretest

Part 1: Identifying Adverbs of Time
Underline the adverb in each sentence that tells *when* or *how often*.

Example: The national anthem is <u>usually</u> sung before sporting events.

1. Sometimes the pool is too crowded to swim laps.

2. First, you must write your name at the top of the paper.

3. I often find my cat sleeping on my bed.

4. The package should have arrived yesterday.

5. The sun always rises in the east and sets in the west.

Part 2: Identifying Adverbs of Place
Underline the adverb in each sentence that tells *where*.

Example: The escalator was going <u>down</u> to the lobby.

6.   I tried walking backward, but I slipped and fell.

7.   The city bus stops here every thirty minutes.

8.   Everyone ran inside when it began to thunder.

9.   It looks like smoke from the wildfires is spreading everywhere.

10.   James walked ahead and found an empty spot for us on the crowded beach.

Unit 9 Pretest

Part 3: Identifying Adverbs of Manner
Underline the adverb in each sentence that tells *how* or in *what manner*.

Example: The elevator doors closed <u>quickly</u> after I stepped inside.

11. Laura spoke happily about her birthday party.

12. The children stood quietly in line as they waited for the bus.

13. Dad stretched his arms and yawned lazily in the hammock.

14. The baby is napping, so please don't speak loudly.

15. My brother proudly showed us the trophy he won at the science fair.

Part 4: Using Adverbs of Time, Place, and Manner in Sentences
Complete each sentence with the kind of adverb requested in parentheses. Example: Please walk to the gymnasium <u>quickly</u>. (adverb of manner)

16. We looked _____ for the missing keys.
     (adverb of place)

17. The children sat around the campfire and talked _____
     _____. (adverb of manner)

18. Max _____ plays tricks on his younger
     brother. (adverb of time)

19. The shoppers moved _____ through the
     crowded mall. (adverb of manner)

20. Jamal _____ misses his weekend soccer
     games. (adverb of time)

Name _____   Date _____

Get Ready

What Is an Adverb?

Adverbs are modifiers that tell *when*, *how often*, *where*, *how*, and *how much*. Adverbs can describe three different parts of speech.

1. Adverbs can modify <u>verbs</u>.
   - Mariana **thinks** *carefully* about her future.
   - Maxwell **can read** long stories *fast*.

2. Adverbs can modify <u>adjectives</u>.
   - David is *definitely* **fun** to be with.
   - At the beach, the sand was *blindingly* **white**.

3. Adverbs can modify <u>other adverbs</u>.
   - Mom can knit a scarf *very* **quickly**.
   - The assignment was completed *quite* **sloppily**.

Adverbs of Time

Adverbs of time answer the questions, "When?" or "How often?"

Leave this room *immediately*!
Leave this room <u>when</u>? *immediately*

Examples include:

again	finally	soon
already	frequently	then
always	now	today
before	often	usually
early	seldom	yesterday
ever	sometimes	

Adverbs of Place

Adverbs of place answer the question, "Where?"

I know I put my glasses *somewhere* in this drawer.
I put my glasses <u>where</u> in this drawer? *somewhere*

Examples include:

above	everywhere	nearby
ahead	forth	out
away	here	somewhere
backward	in	there
below	inside	up
down		

Adverbs of Manner

Adverbs of manner answer the question, "How?" In many cases, you make them by adding an *-ly* to an adjective. For example, if you add *-ly* to the adjective *sharp,* you make the adverb *sharply.*

Reverend Jones spoke to the congregation *calmly*.
Reverend Jones spoke <u>how</u>? *calmly*

Examples include:

beautifully	happily	slowly
carelessly	hard	surely
difficult	laughingly	tiredly
eagerly	nicely	truly
easy	rudely	well
fast	sadly	

Name _____ Date _____

Try It

Write six sentences using adverbs from the Word Bank below. Two sentences should have adverbs of time, two should have adverbs of place, and two should have adverbs of manner. Identify the type of adverb on the line provided.

Word Bank

always	homeward	sluggishly
childishly	nastily	sometimes
daily	never	suddenly
forever	outside	there
forth	rarely	upstairs
goofily	ridiculously	wetly
here	skyward	youthfully

1. _____

_____

Type of adverb: _____

2. _____

_____

Type of adverb: _____

3. _____

_____

Type of adverb: _____

4. _____

   _____

   Type of adverb: _____

5. _____

   _____

   Type of adverb: _____

6. _____

   _____

   Type of adverb: _____

Name _____   Date _____

Get Ready

Three Degrees of Comparison

Adverbs also describe by comparing. Adverbs, like adjectives, have three degrees, or levels, of comparison:

- positive
- comparative
- superlative

The positive degree is the basic building block for the other degrees of comparison. In fact, the positive degree doesn't really compare at all—it just describes. For example,

> We arrived <u>early</u> for our appointment at Town Hall.
> Your sister Anne does her chores <u>cheerfully</u>.

The comparative degree compares two things. Comparative adverbs often end in -*er*, but sometimes they are formed by adding *more* or *less* in front of the positive form. For example,

> We got there <u>earlier</u> than the mayor did!
> Yes, she works <u>more cheerfully</u> than I do in this heat.

The superlative degree compares three or more things. Superlative adverbs often end in -*est*, but sometimes they are formed by adding *most* or *least* in front of their positive form. For example,

> A councilwoman said we had arrived the <u>earliest</u> of all the visitors that week.
> Who does chores the <u>least cheerfully</u> in your family?

Forming Comparatives and Superlatives

How do you know when to add -er or to use *more* or *less* to make a comparative adverb? Or whether to add -est or use *most* or *least* to make a superlative adverb? Here are a few tips to help you decide.

- Adverbs ending in *-ly* in the positive degree usually use *more* for the comparative and *most* for the superlative.

Positive	Comparative	Superlative
sharply	more sharply	most sharply
hopefully	more hopefully	most hopefully

- Adverbs that do not end in *-ly* in the positive degree usually add *-er* for the comparative and *-est* for the superlative.

Positive	Comparative	Superlative
late	later	latest
fast	faster	fastest
well	better	best

- All adverbs use *less* and *least* to show the comparative and superlative degrees of comparison.

Positive	Comparative	Superlative
late	less late	least late
well	less well	least well
sharply	less sharply	least sharply

Name _____   Date _____

Try It

Fill in the missing adverbs in the comparison chart below.

Positive	Comparative	Superlative
1. sweetly	less sweetly	least sweetly
2. far	farther	farthest
3. stubbornly	_____	_____
4. _____	_____	soonest
5. _____	less hungrily	_____
6. near	_____	_____

Name _____   Date _____

Get Ready

In this lesson, you will study two pairs of words that are easy to mix up: *good* and *well,* and *their* and *there.* Make it your goal to use these words correctly, every time!

Good and Well

Sometimes people confuse *good* and *well.* The most common mistake is to use *good* when you should use *well.*

Incorrect: I cleaned my room really good.
Correct: I cleaned my room really well.

You will not have this problem if you keep in mind the differences between adjectives and adverbs, because *good* is an adjective, and *well* is usually an adverb. The chart below compares *good* and *well.*

Good
adjective
modifies a noun or pronoun
tells *what kind of* or *what*
can be a subject complement

Well
usually an adverb
usually modifies a verb
tells *how*

Study these examples.

Becca is a <u>good</u> swimmer. She dives <u>well</u>.
- *What kind of* swimmer is Becca?   *good,* adjective
- *How* does Becca dive?   *well,* adverb

Lemon cake is <u>good</u>. Mother bakes it <u>well</u>.
- Lemon cake is *what?*   *good,* adjective (subject complement)
- *How* does Mother bake it?   *well,* adverb

Their and There

People also confuse *their* and *there*, partly because they are *homophones*— that is, words that sound the same but have different spellings and meanings.

Their is a possessive adjective that means *belonging to them.* For example,

> The Johnsons are taking <u>their</u> vacation this week.
> They are traveling all the way to <u>their</u> own backyard.

There is usually an adverb meaning *in that place.* For example,

> See the camping tent, right <u>there</u> under the oak tree?
> The Johnsons will be sleeping in <u>there</u> all week.

There can also be used before a being verb to begin a sentence or part of a sentence. For example,

> <u>There</u> are not many families who both leave *and* stay home for vacation!
> Say, do you think <u>there</u> is any way we can do the same thing?

Name _____   Date _____

Get Ready

Sometimes people mix up the words *real* and *very*. The most common mistake is to use *real* when you should use *very*.

Incorrect: I cleaned my room real well.
Correct: I cleaned my room very well.

Real is an adjective that means *true, genuine,* or *actual. Very* is an adverb that means *extremely*. Here are examples of how *real* and *very* are used in sentences.

Andy is a <u>real</u> friend to her. He treats her <u>very</u> well.
- *What kind of* friend is Andy?   *real,* adjective
- *How* well does he treat her?   *very,* adverb (modifying an adverb)

The story about the three-legged cat is <u>real</u>. It's <u>very</u> weird, but it's true.
- That story is *what?*   *real,* adjective (subject complement)
- *How* weird is it?   *very,* adverb (modifying an adjective)

The adverb *very* usually modifies only adjectives—for example, *very kind*—or other adverbs—for example, *very happily*. Give two more examples each of *very* modifying adjectives and adverbs.

very modifying an adjective

1. _____
2. _____

very modifying an adverb

1. _____
2. _____

This chart summarizes and compares *real* and *very*.

Real	**Very**
means *genuine, true, actual*	means *extremely*
adjective	adverb
modifies nouns or pronouns	usually modifies only adjectives and adverbs
tells *what kind of* or *what*	tells *how, how much*
can be a subject complement	

Name _____   Date _____

Try It

Analyze and diagram the two sentences on the following pages.

Sentence Analysis Questions
1. Sentence or fragment?
2. Kind of sentence?
3. Verb?
4. Simple subject?
5. Direct object or subject complement?
6. Modifiers?
7. Parts of speech?

Sentence Diagramming Steps

1. **Verb?**
   Write the verb on the main diagram line.

2. **Subject?**
   Write the subject in front of the verb on the main diagram line. Draw a short vertical line (that cuts through the main line) to separate the subject and the verb.

3. **Direct object or subject complement, if any?**
   Write the direct object or subject complement after the verb on the main diagram line. Draw a short vertical (for direct object) or slanted (for subject complement) line between them.

4. **Verb modifiers, if any?**
   Write the modifiers on slanted lines below the verb.

5. **Subject modifiers, if any?**
   Write the modifiers on slanted lines below the subject.

6. **Direct object or subject complement modifiers, if any?**
   Write the modifiers on slanted lines below the direct object or subject complement.

Sentences to Analyze and Diagram

1. Crafty Hailu invited many hungry guests but, cleverly, served no real food!

Sentence or fragment? _____

Kind of sentence? _____

Verb? _____

Simple subject? _____

Direct object or
subject complement? _____

Modifiers? _____

Parts of speech?

Crafty	_____	but	_____
Hailu	_____	cleverly	_____
invited	_____	served	_____
many	_____	no	_____
hungry	_____	real	_____
guests	_____	food	_____

Diagram:

2. Arha finally owned all the promised property.

Sentence or fragment? _____

Kind of sentence? _____

Verb? _____

Simple subject? _____

Direct object or
subject complement? _____

Modifiers? _____

Parts of speech?

Arha	_____	the	_____
finally	_____	promised	_____
owned	_____	property	
all	_____		

Diagram:

Name _____   Date _____

Get Ready

To, Too, and Two

To, too, and two sound the same but are spelled differently and have different meanings. Study them carefully to avoid confusing them with one another.

to   a preposition that tells where
        We are going <u>to</u> the pie-eating contest.

too   an adverb that means *also* or *more than enough*
         Danny wants to join us, <u>too</u>.
         We may have <u>too</u> many people in the car already.

two   a noun or adjective that means *the number 2*
         Last year, Ed ate <u>two</u> dozen pies in the contest!

Negative Words: No, Not, and Never

Can you take the sentence below and make it *negative?* That is, can you rewrite it to deny or negate what it says now?

Apples always grow on trees.

_____

To negate an idea or statement, you need one negative word, such as *no, not, never, none*, or *nothing*.

I can do something to help you get ready.
I can do <u>nothing</u> to help you get ready.

Sue's bike has streamers on the handlebars.
Sue's bike has <u>no</u> streamers on the handlebars.

Look carefully for the adverb *not* as a negative—sometimes it combines with a verb in a contraction and is hard to see.

The Olympic ski team will travel to Norway.
The Olympic ski team <u>won't</u> travel to Norway.

Remember, you only need <u>one</u> negative word to make an idea or statement negative. Don't use two—that's called a *double negative*.

Incorrect: We <u>haven't</u> seen <u>no</u> pink porcupines here.

Correct: We <u>haven't</u> seen pink porcupines here.
                   We have seen <u>no</u> pink porcupines here.

Name _____   Date _____

Try It

Do the following sentences use _to_, _too_, or _two_ and negative words correctly?
Mark each with a ✓ if it is correct and an **X** if it is not.

_____ 1. None of the animals would eat the oats.

_____ 2. Bill is not playing in no baseball game.

_____ 3. She served us to much food.

_____ 4. Haven't you ever seen the ocean?

_____ 5. If you would sing two then we would sound louder.

_____ 6. I'm sorry, but I can't do nothing about it.

Name _____   Date _____

Get Ready

Let's review what you have learned in this unit. Match the numbered items to the correct lettered answers. Write the matching letter on the line next to the number.

Each Who Am I? description will have only one answer. If a lettered answer has an asterisk (*), you will use it twice. One lettered answer will not be used.

Who Am I?

1. _____ I answer the question "When?"

2. _____ I am an adverb that usually modifies only adjectives and other adverbs.

3. _____ I answer the question "How?"

4. _____ I compare two things to one another.

5. _____ I am an adjective that means *genuine* or *true.*

6. _____ We are called negative words.

7. _____ I am the word *well.* What part of speech am I?

8. _____ I end in *-er* or use *more* or *less.*

9. _____ I am an adverb that means *also* or *more than enough.*

10. _____ I am often used with a being verb when I begin a sentence.

11. _____ I am the word *good.* What part of speech am I?

12. _____ I am a preposition that shows motion toward something.

13. _____ I am a noun or adjective that means *the number 2.*

14. _____ I compare three or more things to one another.

15. _____ I am an adverb that means *extremely.*

16. _____ I answer the question "Where?"

17. _____ I am a possessive adjective that means *belonging to them.*

18. _____ I am an adverb that means *in that place.*

19. _____ I end in *-st* or use *most* or *least.*

20. _____ Use only one of us to make an idea negative.

a. their

b. adverb of time

c. very*

d. adverb of place

e. comparative adverb*

f. no, not, never, none, nothing*

g. two

h. superlative adverb*

i. too

j. real

k. adverb of manner

l. there*

m. adjective

n. to

o. positive degree

p. adverb

Name _____ Date _____

Commas After Introductory Words or Phrases

Use a comma to separate an introductory word or phrase from the rest of the sentence.

Commas After Introductory Words

Here are some common introductory words:

afterward	finally	lastly	next
also	first	meanwhile	still
besides	however	nearby	therefore

In general, use a comma after an introductory word.

First, Shanetia made a model of a volcano.

Afterward, she had to scrub lava off the floor.

Still, Shanetia had a lot of fun!

Commas After Introductory Phrases

In general, use a comma after a prepositional phrase that begins a sentence.

During the scary movie, Matthew clutched his teddy bear.

After the last scene, Matthew loosened his tight grip.

Tip: A sentence may begin with two or more prepositional phrases in a row. Place a comma after the last prepositional phrase only.

By the end of the movie, Matthew's bear was squished. (Both *by the end* and *of the movie* are prepositional phrases.)

Place a comma after the introductory word.

1. Next Aunt Merrie poured the batter into the pan.

2. Besides I barely ever get to wear my rain boots.

3. Therefore today was the best day ever!

Place a comma after the introductory phrase.

4. Of my four siblings Ben is the only boy.

5. Between the couch cushions Nadav found the remote control.

6. At the end of the road there is a stop sign.

Place a comma where it is needed in the sentence.

7. Under the red umbrella Marina stayed dry.

8. Finally the alarm clock rang.

9. Nearby a mother robin fed its baby a worm.

Write a sentence that begins with the introductory word or phrase. Be sure to use commas correctly.

10. Of all the seasons _____

_____

11. Meanwhile _____

_____

12. Under the kitchen table _____

_____

Name _____   Date _____

Get Ready

Parts of Speech Review

You have learned seven parts of speech. Here are some of their
letters; fill in the rest of their names and say what each one does.

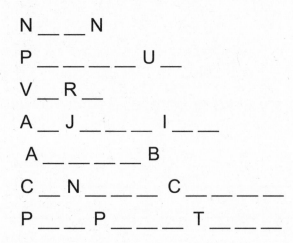

N __ __ N

P __ __ __ __ U __

V __ R __

A __ J __ __ __ I __ __

A __ __ __ __ B

C __ N __ __ __ C __ __ __ __

P __ __ P __ __ __ T __ __ __

Prepositions

Prepositions can point out time, place, direction, and relationship.
You use prepositions every day—here are some common ones.

about	by	onto
above	down	over
across	during	through
after	except	throughout
against	for	to
among	from	toward
around	in	under
at	into	up
before	near	with
beside	of	without
behind	off	
between	on	

Objects of Prepositions and Prepositional Phrases

A preposition relates a noun or pronoun to some other word in a sentence. The noun or pronoun follows the preposition, completes its meaning, and is the *object of the preposition*.

A *phrase* is a group of related words. You have studied *verb phrases,* which consist of two or more verbs working together to do the job of a single verb—for example, *will have stumbled.*

A *prepositional phrase* is a group of related words that begins with a preposition and usually ends with the object of the preposition. Here are some examples of prepositional phrases.

throughout the world
on top
during the night
against your team
with pleasure
above our heads

The words in prepositional phrases work together to do the job of a single modifier. This means that prepositional phrases work as either adjectives or adverbs in sentences.

Name _____   Date _____

Try It: Sentence Analysis

Analyze these sentences. Ask for help if you need it.

Sentence Analysis Questions
1. Sentence or fragment?
2. Kind of sentence?
3. Verb?
4. Simple subject?
5. Direct object or subject complement?
6. Modifiers?
7. Parts of speech?

1. Nobody except Sybil can quickly warn the colonists of the British threat.

Sentence or fragment?   _____

Kind of sentence?   _____

Verb?   _____

Simple subject?   _____

Direct object or
subject complement?   _____

Modifiers?   _____

Parts of speech?

Nobody	_____	colonists	_____
except	_____	of	_____
Sybil	_____	the	_____
can warn	_____	British	_____
quickly	_____	threat	_____
the	_____		

2. People were repeating the story of the girl's heroic night ride with admiration.

Sentence or fragment? _____

Kind of sentence? _____

Verb? _____

Simple subject? _____

Direct object or
subject complement? _____

Modifiers? _____

Parts of speech?

People	_____	girl's	_____
were repeating	_____	heroic	_____
the	_____	night	_____
story	_____	ride	_____
of	_____	with	_____
the	_____	admiration	_____

Name _____ Date _____

Get Ready

Let's review what you have learned about prepositions and prepositional phrases. Circle the correct answers.

1. A phrase is a group of _____ words.

   related   irrelevant   reflecting

2. Words that relate nouns or pronouns to another word in a sentence are called

   prepositions   preposterous   presents

3. The noun or pronoun that follows a preposition is called the _____ of the preposition.

   objection   obstinate   object

4. A preposition and its object form a prepositional _____.

   fraction   phrase   phoneme

5. A prepositional phrase may contain many words, but it does the job of a single_____.

   moderator   modernizer   modifier

6. Which of the following words are prepositions?

   apple   inside   icky   through   throat
   across   toward   tower   the   pretty
   crashed   near   and   swerve   among

Name _____ Date _____

Try It: Sentence Analysis

Analyze and diagram these sentences. Ask for help if you need it.

Sentence Analysis Questions

1. Sentence or fragment?
2. Kind of sentence?
3. Verb?
4. Simple subject?
5. Direct object or subject complement?
6. Modifiers?
7. Parts of speech?

Sentence Diagramming Steps

1. **Verb?**
   Write the verb on the main diagram line.

2. **Subject?**
   Write the subject in front of the verb on the main diagram line. Draw a short vertical line (that cuts through the main line) to separate the subject and the verb.

3. **Direct object or subject complement, if any?**
   Write the direct object or subject complement after the verb on the main diagram line. Draw a short vertical (for direct object) or slanted (for subject complement) line between them.

4. **Verb modifiers, if any?**
   Write the modifiers on slanted lines below the verb.

5. **Subject modifiers, if any?**
   Write the modifiers on slanted lines below the subject.

6. **Direct object or subject complement modifiers, if any?**
   Write the modifiers on slanted lines below the direct object or subject complement.

1. The last real live dragon can breathe fire and smoke.

Sentence or fragment?   _____

Kind of sentence?   _____

Verb?   _____

Simple subject?   _____

Direct object or
subject complement?   _____

Modifiers?   _____

Parts of speech?

The	_____	can breathe	_____
last	_____	fire	_____
real	_____	and	_____
live	_____	smoke	_____
dragon	_____		

Diagram:

2. May I kill the fierce dragon and rescue the silly prince?

Sentence or fragment? _____

Kind of sentence? _____

Verb? _____

Simple subject? _____

Direct object or
subject complement? _____

Modifiers? _____

Parts of speech?

May kill	_____	and	_____
I	_____	rescue	_____
the	_____	the	_____
fierce	_____	silly	_____
dragon	_____	prince	_____

Diagram:

Name _____   Date _____

Get Ready

Let's take a closer look at a few prepositions.

Between and *Among*

Use *between* when you are discussing <u>two</u> people, places, things, or ideas, or <u>two groups</u> of people, places, things, or ideas. For example,

> There are six houses and ten trees <u>between you and me</u>.
> Please put the rubies <u>between the sapphires and emeralds</u>.

Use *among* when you are discussing <u>more than two</u> people, places, things, or ideas. For example,

> <u>Among all her friends</u>, Julio is the most reliable.
> Bill had a hard time choosing <u>among all the college courses</u>.

How can you remember when to use *between* and *among*? Here are a couple of tips to jog your memory:

- You use *between* when referring to two of something. Look—the letters *tw* appear in both words: be*tw*een and *tw*o.

- You use *among* when referring to many. Remember the *m* in *m*any and a*m*ong.

From and *Off*

From and *off* both relate to distance or separation, but they aren't synonyms.

From can show the source of something.
> We buy our corn <u>from</u> the farmers' market.
> Is that box a present <u>from</u> Aunt Jean?

From can also help show distance in space or time.
> Labor Day is three weeks <u>from</u> today.
> California is thousands of miles <u>from</u> Georgia.

Off, when used as a preposition, can mean "down from" or "away from."
> The circus performer fell <u>off</u> the tightrope.
> Hey, cat, get <u>off</u> the hood of the car!

It is unnecessary and incorrect to use the preposition *of* after another preposition, such as *inside, outside,* or *off.*

Incorrect:	The squirrel leaped off of the roof.
Correct:	The squirrel leaped off the roof.

Practice with the prepositions *between, among, from,* and *off* in the exercises in your workbook, *Exercises in English.*

Name _____   Date _____

Try It

Sentence Diagramming Steps

1. Verb?
Write the verb on the main diagram line.

2. Subject?
Write the subject in front of the verb on the main diagram line. Draw a short vertical line (that cuts through the main line) to separate the subject and the verb.

3. Direct object or subject complement, if any?
Write the direct object or subject complement after the verb on the main diagram line. Draw a short vertical (for direct object) or slanted (for subject complement) line between them.

4. Verb modifiers, if any?
Write the modifiers on slanted lines below the verb.

5. Subject modifiers, if any?
Write the modifiers on slanted lines below the subject.

6. Direct object or subject complement modifiers, if any?
Write the modifiers on slanted lines below the direct object or subject complement.

Diagram these two sentences. Ask for help if you need it.

1. His daughter became a most skillful, most sensible princess.

2. The extremely kind prince and very merciful princess did not kill the poor old dragon.

Name _____ Date _____

Get Ready

A *phrase* is a group of related words. You just studied *prepositional phrases*, which can do the job of a single modifier.

Which two parts of speech are modifiers?
Adjectives and adverbs.

Today we'll take a look at prepositional phrases that do the job of adjectives. They are called *adjectival phrase*s.

Which two parts of speech do you think adjectival phrases modify?

That's right; they modify nouns or pronouns. Look at these sentences. The nouns (in bold) are described by the circled adjectival phrases.

1. Do you see the **girl** with the black headband and red shirt?

2. The **lamp** near the old couch is broken.

3. **Everybody** except you is going.

Where is the adjectival phrase in relation to the word it describes?

To summarize, an adjectival phrase
- is a prepositional phrase
- contains a preposition, at least one object, and any words modifying the object(s)
- works as an adjective
- always follows right after the noun or pronoun it modifies

Name _____   Date _____

Get Ready

Review

A *phrase* is a group of related words that acts as a single part of speech. A prepositional phrase begins with a preposition, ends with an object, and includes any words that modify the object. For example,

in the good old summertime

Sometimes a prepositional phrase has more than one object. For example,

over hill and dale

Adverbial Phrases

You have studied prepositional phrases that act like adjectives. Now, let's turn to prepositional phrases that do the job of adverbs: *adverbial phrases*.

Adverbial phrases can modify verbs, adjectives, or other adverbs. In this lesson, we will focus on adverbial phrases that modify verbs.

Look at these sentences with adverbial phrases. The verbs (in bold) are described by the circled adverbial phrases.

1. The frightened cat **scrambled** up the oak tree.

2. From the empty room **came** strange noises.

3. I **looked** inside the drawer, but couldn't find the missing sock.

Notice the position of the adverbial phrase. Unlike adjectival phrases, which always follow immediately after the words they modify, adverbial phrases can appear anywhere in sentences.

To summarize, an adverbial phrase
- is a prepositional phrase
- contains a preposition, at least one object, and any words modifying the object(s)
- works as an adverb
- modifies a verb, adjective, or other adverb
- can appear anywhere in a sentence

Name _____   Date _____

Get Ready

Fill in the blanks to show what you have learned about adverbial and adjectival phrases.

1. A _____ is a group of related words that acts as a single part of speech.

2. A prepositional phrase begins with a _____, ends with an _____ that is a noun or pronoun, and includes any words that modify the object.

3. Prepositional phrases can be _____, which means that they modify a noun or pronoun.

4. Prepositional phrases can also be _____, which means that they modify a verb, adjective, or other adverb.

5. A prepositional phrase that is _____ can be anywhere in a sentence.

6. A prepositional phrase that is _____, on the other hand, always appears right after the word it modifies.

Name _____   Date _____

Try It

Read these sentences. Circle the adjectival phrases, and underline the adverbial phrases.

Examples:
Eleanor read a book (on meerkats) yesterday.
She reads about animals <u>during the evening</u>.

1. A meerkat is a small creature with long, soft fur.

2. Meerkats live in underground burrows.

3. They often sit or stand near their burrows.

4. Meerkats belong to the mongoose family.

5. Members of the mongoose family are carnivores.

6. In the South African language Afrikaans, meerkat means "lake cat."

Name   Date

Commas After Introductory Words or Phrases

Use a comma to separate an introductory word or phrase from the rest of the sentence.

Commas After Introductory Words

Here are some common introductory words:

afterward	finally	lastly	next
also	first	meanwhile	still
besides	however	nearby	therefore

In general, use a comma after an introductory word.

First, Shanetia made a model of a volcano.

Afterward, she had to scrub lava off the floor.

Still, Shanetia had a lot of fun!

Commas After Introductory Phrases

In general, use a comma after a prepositional phrase that begins a sentence.

During the scary movie, Matthew clutched his teddy bear.

After the last scene, Matthew loosened his tight grip.

Tip: A sentence may begin with two or more prepositional phrases in a row. Place a comma after the last prepositional phrase only.

By the end of the movie, Matthew's bear was squished. (Both *by the end* and *of the movie* are prepositional phrases.)

Place a comma after the introductory word.

1. Next Aunt Merrie poured the batter into the pan.

2. Besides I barely ever get to wear my rain boots.

3. Therefore today was the best day ever!

Place a comma after the introductory phrase.

4. Of my four siblings Ben is the only boy.

5. Between the couch cushions Nadav found the remote control.

6. At the end of the road there is a stop sign.

Place a comma where it is needed in the sentence.

7. Under the red umbrella Marina stayed dry.

8. Finally the alarm clock rang.

9. Nearby a mother robin fed its baby a worm.

Write a sentence that begins with the introductory word or phrase. Be sure to use commas correctly.

10. Of all the seasons _____

_____

11. Meanwhile _____

_____

12. Under the kitchen table _____

_____

Name _____   Date _____

Try It

Let's review what you've learned about prepositions, prepositional phrases, adverbial phrases, and adjectival phrases. Answer the following questions.

Part 1: Identifying Prepositional Phrases in Sentences
Underline the prepositional phrase(s) in each sentence.
Example: I placed my suitcases and shoe boxes <u>under my bed.</u>

1. We could not take pictures during the performance.

2. The scouts followed their leaders into the forest.

3. The streets were flooded after the thunderstorm.

4. Jonathan jumped off the diving board and into the swimming pool.

Part 2: Using Prepositional Phrases in Sentences
Complete each sentence with a prepositional phrase.
Example: The chef sprinkled powdered sugar   <u>on the cookies.</u>

5. New train tracks were built_____.

6. Mr. Hilling plans to ride his motorcycle_____.

7. We enjoyed picking peaches and pears_____.

8. When the fire alarm sounds, please walk quietly_____.

Part 3: Using *Between*, *Among*, *From*, and *Off* Correctly in Sentences
Circle the correct preposition to complete each sentence.

Example: The argument was_____the two older boys.
(a.) between
b. among

9. My three sisters often share clothes_____themselves.
   a. between
   b. among

10. I couldn't get the top_____the jar of peanut butter.
    a. off
    b. off of

11. We buy brown eggs_____Mr. Topping every Saturday.
    a. from
    b. off

12. Please sit_____Nancy and me at the football game.
    a. between
    b. among

13. Eleanor fell_____the balance beam several times during her gymnastics class.
    a. off
    b. from

14. A small creek flows_____the library and the bank.
    a. between
    b. among

Part 4: Identifying Adverbial Phrases

Underline the adverbial phrase in each sentence.
On the blank line, write the verb the phrase modifies.
Example: My lunch money fell <u>out of my pocket</u>.   fell _____

15. We pushed our bicycles into the garage.   _____

16. Anita sat on the bed as she tied her shoes.   _____

17. I bought daisies at the flower shop.   _____

Part 5: Identifying Adjectival Phrases in Sentences

Underline the adjectival phrase in each sentence.
On the blank line, write the noun the phrase modifies.
Example: The butterflies <u>in the painting</u> looked real.   butterflies _____

18. Timothy doesn't like the freckles on his nose.   _____

19. The streetlight behind my house is very bright.   _____

20. The bread in the pantry is stale.   _____

Part 6: Distinguishing Between Adjectival and Adverbial Phrases in Sentences

Read each sentence. Is the italicized phrase adjectival or adverbial?
Circle the correct answer.

21. The quilt *on my bed* was my great-grandmother's.
    a. adjectival
    b. adverbial

22. The statue *in the park* was built to honor Dr. Martin Luther King.
    a. adjectival
    b. adverbial

23. My mother reached *into her purse* to get her keys.
    a. adjectival
    b. adverbial

24. The train was going *to Washington, D.C., and Philadelphia.*
    a. adjectival
    b. adverbial

25. The ground *under the bleachers* was covered with litter.
    a. adjectival
    b. adverbial

Name _____ Date _____

Get Ready

What Is a Conjunction?

A *conjunction* is a word that joins words or groups of words. Three of the most common conjunctions are *and, but*, and *or*.

And, but, and *or* have quite different meanings. The examples below will help you use the right conjunction to say what you want to say.

- ***And*** joins ideas that are <u>similar</u> or <u>equal</u>.
  He *and* Paul are best friends.

- ***But*** joins ideas that are <u>different</u> or show a <u>contrast</u>.
  JoAnne can skateboard, *but* she can't jump rope.

- ***Or*** joins ideas that give a <u>choice</u> or <u>alternative</u>.
  I can't decide whether to play checkers *or* chess.

Connecting Subjects with Conjunctions

If a sentence has more than one subject, it has a *compound subject*. Conjunctions usually join the subjects.

The following sentences have compound subjects. The subjects are underlined, and the conjunctions are circled.

<u>Betsy</u> (and) her <u>father</u> are taking the train to Washington, D.C.

<u>Cats</u> (or) <u>dogs</u> are common house pets.

<u>Sun</u> (but) not <u>heat</u> is what I like.

Connecting Predicates with Conjunctions

You can also join predicates with conjunctions. Remember that the *predicate* tells what the subject is or does. The most important word in the predicate is the *verb*.

If a sentence has more than one verb, it has a *compound predicate*.

The following sentences have compound predicates. The compound verbs are underlined, and the conjunctions are circled.

The baby-sitter <u>is diapering</u> Tommy (and) <u>is dressing</u> Becca.

Uncle Jim usually <u>swims</u> (or) <u>runs</u> to stay in shape.

She <u>complained</u> a lot (but) eventually <u>did help</u> clean the barn.

Name _____ Date _____

Correlative Conjunctions

Correlative conjunctions are conjunctions that work in pairs to connect parts of sentences. Examples are *either/or*, *neither/nor*, and *both/and*.

Correlative conjunctions can connect subjects.

Both Quinn **and** Erik live in my neighborhood.

Correlative conjunctions can connect predicates.

The puppy can **neither** sit **nor** stay for very long.

Correlative conjunctions can connect sentences.

For the talent show, **either** I'll sing a ballad, **or** I'll walk on my hands.

Tip: Correlative conjunctions may also connect other parts of speech, such as direct objects.

Circle the correlative conjunctions. Underline the parts of the compound subject.

1. Neither Mom nor Dad ate ice cream for breakfast.

2. Tonight both the moon and the stars are shining brightly.

Circle the correlative conjunctions. Underline the parts of the compound predicate.

3. Ian both laughed and snorted at the same time.

4. Evie is either cooking dinner or doing a science experiement.

Circle the correlative conjunctions. Underline the sentences they connect.

5. Either send Uncle Dante a thank-you note, or call him on the phone.

Use correlative conjunctions to complete the sentence.

6. _____ you _____ I have pigtails today.

7. Meg _____ ran a mile _____ swam for 20 minutes.

Write a sentence with the pair of correlative conjunctions. Circle the correlating conjunctions, and underline the words they connect.

8. both/and

_____

_____

9. either/or

_____

_____

10. neither/nor

_____

_____

Name _____   Date _____

Get Ready

Review
Can you answer these questions?

- What is the function of a conjunction?
- Can you name the three most common conjunctions?
- The three conjunctions you named have different purposes—what are they?

Connecting Direct Objects with Conjunctions
If a sentence has more than one direct object receiving the action of the verb, it has a *compound direct object*. Conjunctions link the direct objects.

The following sentences have compound direct objects. The compound direct objects are underlined, and the conjunctions are circled.

Tonight Dad is cooking <u>macaroni</u> (and) <u>cheese</u>.

Would you like to drink <u>milk</u> (or) <u>water</u> with supper?

Naida likes <u>cookies</u> (but) not <u>cake</u> for dessert.

Practice using compound direct objects and conjunctions in your *Exercises in English* workbook.

Name _____   Date _____

Try It: Sentence Analysis

Analyze the following two sentences. Ask for help if you need it.

Sentence Analysis Questions
1. Sentence or fragment?
2. Kind of sentence?
3. Verb?
4. Simple subject?
5. Direct object or subject complement?
6. Modifiers?
7. Parts of speech?

1. The horse of power has eyes of fire and hoofs of iron.

Sentence or fragment?   _____

Kind of sentence?   _____

Verb?   _____

Simple subject?   _____

Direct object or
subject complement?   _____

Modifiers?   _____

Parts of speech?   The   _____   of   _____
                     horse _____   fire _____
                     of   _____   and   _____
                     power _____   hoofs _____
                     has   _____   of   _____
                     eyes   _____   iron _____

2. The archer and Vasilissa married and lived together for many happy years.

Sentence or fragment? _____

Kind of sentence? _____

Verb? _____

Simple subject? _____

Direct object or
subject complement? _____

Modifiers? _____

Parts of speech?

The	_____	lived	_____
archer	_____	together	_____
and	_____	for	_____
Vasilissa	_____	many	_____
married	_____	happy	_____
and	_____	years	_____

Name _____ Date _____

Get Ready

Review

Fill in the blanks.

1. The role of a conjunction is to _____ words or groups of words.

2. Conjunctions can make _____ subjects, predicates, or direct objects.

3. a. **Box** the conjunction below that joins ideas that are *choices or alternatives*.

   b. **Underline** the conjunction below that joins ideas that are *different or contrasting*.

   c. **Circle** the conjunction below that joins ideas that are *alike or similar*.

oar	or	for
am	and	an
but	by	beside

Connecting Sentences with Conjunctions

You have learned how to connect parts of sentences using conjunctions. Did you realize that you could connect entire sentences with conjunctions?

A conjunction can join related sentences to form a *compound sentence*.

When you combine two sentences, replace the end punctuation of the first sentence with a comma.

Look at these sentences. Each sentence in part B is a compound sentence formed by combining the sentences in part A.

1. A. Luke has a ball python. He keeps it in a cage.

    B. Luke has a ball python, <u>and</u> he keeps it in a cage.

2. A. Luke might give the snake away. Rina might take care of the snake while Luke is away.

    B. Luke might give the snake away, <u>or</u> Rina might take care of the snake while Luke is away.

3. A. I don't know whether I'd like that snake as a pet. It is easy to take care of.

    B. I don't know whether I'd like that snake as a pet, <u>but</u> it is easy to take care of.

Name _____   Date _____

Try It

All the following sentences contain compound elements, but only some are compound sentences. Mark the compound sentences CS.

Bonus: After you have found the compound sentences, explain whether the other sentences contain compound subjects, compound direct objects, or compound predicates.

Examples:
_____ Robin Hood and his outlaws roamed Sherwood Forest. *(compound subject)*
_CS_ Some praised them, but some blamed them.

_____ 1. People sang many songs and stories about Robin Hood.

_____ 2. Robin Hood was kind to the poor, and many loved him for it.

_____ 3. No longer a bridegroom, Allin-a-Dale sighed heavily but kept walking.

_____ 4. The fair maiden dreaded marrying the old man, but her father was forcing her to.

_____ 5. Robin Hood declared, "Do you want to marry this man or that man?"

_____ 6. The young couple was joyous, but the rich man went home furious.

Name _____ Date _____

Get Ready

Ugh!   Yikes!   Hooray!   Oh no!   Man!   Wow!

Have you ever used expressions like these? If so, you have used *interjections*. An interjection is a word or phrase that expresses strong feeling, such as surprise, excitement, anger, or fear.

Interjections are frequently exclamations that interrupt, or are separate from, the other thoughts expressed.

Here are a few more popular interjections. What are some of your favorites?

Ouch!   Nice!   Hey!   Rats!   Cool!   Yecch!

Really!   That's awesome!   Goodness gracious!

As you can see from the examples, interjections are usually one word or a very short exclamatory sentence. They are often written independently. Sometimes, though, the interjection appears as part of a sentence, separated from the rest of the sentence by a comma or dash.

Uh-oh, who spilled the ink on the wedding gown?
Hey, look at that cat jump.

The emotion an interjection expresses can vary with how it is used. Some of the feelings an interjection can show include:

joy	We won! Hurrah!
impatience	Well, come on!
wonder	Boy! I never saw such a thing.
pain	Ow! That stings!

caution or warning	<u>Say</u>, you better not go there!
surprise	<u>What</u>! Do I see a purple cow?
fear	<u>Help</u>! Let's get out of here!
disgust	Look at that squishy brown thing—<u>ick</u>!
anger or distress	<u>So</u>! This is how you repay me?
sorrow	<u>Alas</u>, my life is over!

Practice using interjections in your workbook, *Exercises in English*.

Name _____   Date _____

Try It: Sentence Diagramming

Sentence Diagramming Steps

1. Verb?
Write the verb on the main diagram line.

2. Subject?
Write the subject in front of the verb on the main diagram line. Draw a short vertical line (that cuts through the main line) to separate the subject and the verb.

3. Direct object or subject complement, if any?
Write the direct object after the verb on the main diagram line. Draw a short vertical (for direct object) or slanted (for subject complement) line between them.

4. Verb modifiers, if any?
Write the modifiers on slanted lines below the verb.

5. Subject modifiers, if any?
Write the modifiers on slanted lines below the subject.

6. Direct object or subject complement modifiers, if any?
Write the modifiers on slanted lines below the direct object or subject complement.

7. Modifiers of modifiers, if any?
Write the modifiers below the words they modify on L-shaped lines.

8. Prepositional phrases? Write them below the words they modify, with the preposition on a slanted line and its object on a connected horizontal line.

Diagram these three sentences. Ask for help if you need it.

1. The Cherokee did not have a written language.

2. Finally, Sequoyah invented a written language of signs.

3. Each sign in this new writing represented a certain spoken sound.

Name   Date

Correlative Conjunctions

Correlative conjunctions are conjunctions that work in pairs to connect parts of sentences. Examples are *either/or*, *neither/nor*, and *both/and*.

Correlative conjunctions can connect subjects.

Both Quinn **and** Erik live in my neighborhood.

Correlative conjunctions can connect predicates.

The puppy can **neither** sit **nor** stay for very long.

Correlative conjunctions can connect sentences.

For the talent show, **either** I'll sing a ballad, **or** I'll walk on my hands.

Tip: Correlative conjunctions may also connect other parts of speech, such as direct objects.

Circle the correlative conjunctions. Underline the parts of the compound subject.

1. Neither Mom nor Dad ate ice cream for breakfast.

2. Tonight both the moon and the stars are shining brightly.

Circle the correlative conjunctions. Underline the parts of the compound predicate.

3. Ian both laughed and snorted at the same time.

4. Evie is either cooking dinner or doing a science experiement.

Circle the correlative conjunctions. Underline the sentences they connect.

5. Either send Uncle Dante a thank-you note, or call him on the phone.

Use correlative conjunctions to complete the sentence.

6. _____ you _____ I have pigtails today.

7. Meg _____ ran a mile _____ swam for 20 minutes.

Write a sentence with the pair of correlative conjunctions. Circle the correlating conjunctions, and underline the words they connect.

8. both/and

_____

_____

_____

9. either/or

_____

_____

_____

10. neither/nor

_____

_____

_____

Name _____   Date _____

Get Ready

Who Am I?
Match the lettered names to their descriptions.

_____ 1.   I am a preposition you use to speak of two people, places, things, or ideas.

_____ 2.   I am a preposition you use to speak of more than two people, places, things, or ideas.

_____ 3.   I am made of a preposition, an object, and any modifiers of the object.

_____ 4.   I am a prepositional phrase that modifies a noun or pronoun.

_____ 5.   I am a prepositional phrase that modifies a verb, adjective, or other adverb.

_____ 6.   I am a part of speech that connects words or groups of words.

_____ 7.   I show feelings such as disgust, joy, fear, pain, or amazement.

_____ 8.   I describe subjects, predicates, direct objects, or sentences that have been joined by a conjunction.

_____ 9.   I connect ideas that are equal or similar.

_____ 10. I connect ideas that offer alternatives or choices.

_____ 11. I connect ideas that are different or contrasting.

a. conjunction
b. prepositional phrase
c. among
d. and
e. adverbial phrase
f. but

g. compound
h. between
i. interjection
j. or
k. adjectival phrase

Name _____   Date _____

Get Ready

This unit will weave together much of the grammar you have learned all year. As you complete the lessons, you will both review and learn new things about sentences.

Subjects

The *subject* of a sentence is who or what the sentence is about. The *complete subject* is a noun or pronoun and all of its modifiers. The most important word in the subject is the noun or pronoun. This noun or pronoun is called the *simple subject*. Sometimes the subject and the simple subject are the same.

To find a subject, ask *who* or *what* about the verb. In Sentences 1 and 2 below, the subjects are underlined once and the simple subjects are underlined twice.

1. The main character in *Harriet the Spy* plans to be a famous author someday.

2. She practices by following a spy route and writing down what she sees every day.

Now it's your turn: Underline the subjects and simple subjects in Sentences 3 and 4.

3. A secret notebook holds all her notes and information.

4. She plans for the next day's spying at bedtime each night.

Predicates

The predicate of a sentence tells more about what the subject is or does. The *complete predicate* contains the verb and all its modifiers, direct objects, or subject complements. The most important word in the predicate is the verb, which is also called the *simple predicate*. Sometimes the predicate and the simple predicate are the same.

To find a predicate, ask, "What does the sentence tell about the subject?" In Sentences 5 and 6 below, the predicates are underlined once and the simple predicates are underlined twice.

5. Some of her classmates <u>find her spy notebook, unfortunately</u>.

6. They <u>turn the tables on Harriet</u>.

Now, underline the predicates and simple predicates in Sentences 7 and 8.

7. The other children spy on her instead!

8. Everybody is friends again in the end, though.

Complete Sentence or Fragment?

A *sentence* is a group of words that expresses a complete thought. A sentence has two parts: a subject and a predicate.

This is a sentence:

Harriet admitted her mistakes.

A *fragment* is a group of words that does not express a complete thought. A fragment may be missing a subject, a predicate, or possibly both. Even if it begins with a capital letter and ends in a period, a fragment is not a sentence.

This is a fragment:

The author Louise Fitzhugh.

Which groups of words below are complete sentences, and which are fragments? Discuss your answers.

9.   That day, after school.

10. She put on her spy clothes.

11. The murmur of a voice through the door.

12. She wrote a long account of what she had seen.

13. Sat in her bathtub taking her bath before dinner.

<u>Name</u> _____   Date _____

Get Ready

The *subject* of a sentence is the person, place, thing, or idea that the sentence is about. To find a subject, ask who or what about the verb.

The *complete subject* is <u>all</u> the words that name and describe who or what the sentence is about—that is, the subject noun or pronoun and all its modifiers.

The subject modifiers can include adjectives and adjectival phrases. The complete subject of the sentence below is underlined. It includes two adjectives and one adjectival phrase—name them.

   <u>A butterscotch sundae with cherries</u> is Mom's favorite.

The *simple subject* is the subject noun or pronoun without any modifiers.

   A butterscotch (sundae) with cherries is Mom's favorite.

Underline the complete subject and circle the simple subject in this sentence.

   A fresh slice of dark chocolate cake is what Dad prefers.

Practice finding complete and simple subjects in sentences in your *Exercises in English* workbook.

Name _____   Date _____

Try It: Sentence Analysis

Analyze these sentences. Ask for help if you need it.

Sentence Analysis Questions
1. Sentence or fragment?
2. Kind of sentence?
3. Verb?
4. Simple subject?
5. Direct object or subject complement?
6. Modifiers?
7. Parts of speech?

1. Left her father and mother and the land of her birth.

Sentence or fragment?   _____

Kind of sentence?   _____

Verb?   _____

Simple subject?   _____

Direct object or
subject complement?   _____

Modifiers?   _____

Parts of speech?

Left	_____	the	_____
her	_____	land	_____
father	_____	of	_____
and	_____	her	_____
mother	_____	birth	_____
and	_____		

2. The devoted Ruth will go to a strange country with her beloved Naomi.

Sentence or fragment? _____

Kind of sentence? _____

Verb? _____

Simple subject? _____

Direct object or
subject complement? _____

Modifiers? _____

_____

Parts of speech?

The	_____	strange	_____
devoted	_____	country	_____
Ruth	_____	with	_____
will go	_____	her	_____
to	_____	beloved	_____
a	_____	Naomi	_____

3. Can any pretty dress or ornament in the world outshine the goodness in her face?

Sentence or fragment? _____

Kind of sentence? _____

Verb? _____

Simple subject? _____

Direct object or
subject complement? _____

Modifiers? _____

_____

Parts of speech?

any	_____	world	_____
pretty	_____	can outshine	_____
dress	_____	The	_____
or	_____	goodness	_____
ornament	_____	In	_____
in	_____	Her	_____
the	_____	face	_____

Name _____   Date _____

Get Ready

The *predicate* of a sentence tells more about the subject—what it is or does.

The *complete predicate* includes the verb and all of its modifiers, as well as any direct objects or subject complements. The verb's modifiers include adverbs and adverbial phrases.

The complete predicate of the sentence below has been underlined. It has three adverbial phrases—name them.

Our family <u>sweats for two weeks in Georgia in July</u>.

The *simple predicate* is the verb without any modifiers.

Our family (sweats) for two weeks in Georgia in July.

Underline the complete predicate and circle the simple predicate in the sentence below.

I want to go somewhere cooler, like the Arctic, instead.

Practice finding complete and simple predicates in more sentences in *Exercises in English*.

Name _____   Date _____

Try It

Sentence Diagramming Steps

1. Verb?
Write the verb on the main diagram line.

2. Subject?
Write the subject in front of the verb on the main diagram line. Draw a short vertical line (that cuts through the main line) to separate the subject and the verb.

3. Direct object or subject complement, if any?
Write the direct object or subject complement after the verb on the main diagram line. Draw a short vertical (for direct object) or slanted (for subject complement) line between them.

4. Verb modifiers, if any?
Write the modifiers on slanted lines below the verb.

5. Subject modifiers, if any?
Write the modifiers on slanted lines below the subject.

6. Direct object or subject complement modifiers, if any?
Write the modifiers on slanted lines below the direct object or subject complement.

7. Modifiers of modifiers, if any?
Write the modifiers below the words they modify on L-shaped lines.

8. Prepositional phrases?
Write the phrases below the words they modify, with the preposition on a slanted line and its object on a connected horizontal line.

Diagram these three sentences. Ask for help if you need it.

1. Little David was the only volunteer against the Philistine Goliath.

2. The shepherd boy had no weapons except his staff and his slingshot.

3. A stone whizzed through the air and knocked the giant down.

Name _____   Date _____

Get Ready

How is writing like chemistry or cooking? Well, in all three you mix elements to create compounds. The adjective *compound* means "made from a mixture of two or more parts or ingredients." The recipe for creating a *compound subject* is to mix together two or more subjects, and the recipe for a *compound predicate* is to combine two or more verbs.

Compound Subjects

When a sentence with one verb has two or more simple subjects, it has a *compound subject*. Conjunctions join the subjects. In this sentence with a compound subject, the subjects are underlined and the conjunction is circled.

> She and I will serve turkey dinners to homeless people at Thanksgiving.

Compound Predicates

When a sentence with one subject has more than one verb, it has a *compound predicate*. Conjunctions join the verbs in a compound predicate. In this sentence with a compound predicate, the verbs are underlined and the conjunction is circled.

> The blueberry pie is hissing, bubbling, and steaming in the oven.

Add Style to Your Writing

Why do we need compound subjects and predicates? It would be pretty boring to eat the same food every day. Sometimes you crave variety. And sometimes you simply need more than one subject or verb to get across a complete idea. For example,

- *Compound subject*:
  Oats, peas, beans, and barley grow in our garden.

- *Compound predicate*:
  Do you roast, broil, or grill your steaks?

Good cooks fix a variety of interesting, healthy foods. Likewise, good writers use a variety of techniques with words. Compound subjects or predicates add variety and strengthen your writing. At times it sounds better to combine two or more short, related sentences into one longer, flowing sentence.

Try it yourself. How would you rewrite these three choppy sentences to make one smoother sentence with a compound subject?

1. Jack is making chicken and dumplings. Lila is also making chicken and dumplings. Elaine is making chicken and dumplings too.

   _____

   _____

   _____

Or these three sentences into one sentence with a compound predicate?

2. My grandfather squeezed fresh orange juice for our breakfast. He served us sandwiches for lunch. Then Grandfather cooked eggplant parmesan for supper.

   _____

   _____

   _____

   _____

Name _____   Date _____

Get Ready

If a microscope uses two or more lenses to magnify objects, it is a compound microscope. If a sentence has two or more direct objects receiving the action of one verb, the sentence has a *compound direct object*. Conjunctions link the direct objects.

Remember that direct objects occur only in sentences with action verbs.

In these examples the compound direct objects are underlined, and the conjunctions are circled.

- That movie always makes <u>my brother</u> and <u>me</u> cry.

- Could we borrow a <u>tissue</u> or <u>handkerchief</u>?

- When I cry, you might hear a <u>sniffle</u> but never a <u>snort</u>.

Practice using compound direct objects in *Exercises in English*.

Name _____   Date _____

Try It: Sentence Analysis

Analyze the following three sentences. Watch for compound elements!
Ask for help, if you need it.

Sentence Analysis Questions
1. Sentence or fragment?
2. Kind of sentence?
3. Verb?
4. Simple subject?
5. Direct object or subject complement?
6. Modifiers?
7. Parts of speech?

1. The Egyptian pharaoh's daughter will find Moses in the bulrushes and will help him and his family.

Sentence or fragment?   _____

Kind of sentence?   _____

Verb?   _____

Simple subject?   _____

Direct object or
subject complement?   _____

Modifiers?   _____

Parts of speech?

The	_____	bulrushes	_____
Egyptian	_____	and	_____
pharoah's	_____	will help	_____
daughter	_____	him	_____
will find	_____	and	_____
Moses	_____	his	_____
in	_____	family	_____
the	_____		

2. The voice from the burning bush is speaking to Moses about a land of milk and honey!

Sentence or fragment? _____

Kind of sentence? _____

Verb? _____

Simple subject? _____

Direct object or
subject complement? _____

Modifiers? _____

_____

Parts of speech?

The	_____	Moses	_____
voice	_____	about	_____
from	_____	a	_____
the	_____	land	_____
burning	_____	of	_____
bush	_____	milk	_____
is speaking	_____	and	_____
to	_____	honey	_____

3. A great wind parted the rough waters and Moses led the Israelites through safely.

Sentence or fragment? _____

Kind of sentence? _____

Verb? _____

Simple subject? _____

Direct object or
subject complement? _____

Modifiers? _____

_____

Parts of speech?

A	_____	and	_____
great		Moses	
wind	_____	led	_____
parted	_____	the	_____
the	_____	Israelites	_____
rough	_____	through	_____
waters	_____	safely	_____

Name _____   Date _____

Get Ready

Here's a chance to show how well you recognize compound elements in sentences. Read Sentences A-C and then answer Questions 1-3.

A. In Italy, hosts often serve fruit or cheese for dessert.
B. Pasta and meat are typical Italian foods.
C. Many Italians eat the main meal at midday and then rest.

1. Which sentence has a compound subject?   _____
2. Which sentence has a compound predicate?   _____
3. Which sentence has a compound direct object?   _____

Now, you'll have a chance to add compound elements to a sentence. Here's the sentence.

D. The blue jay pulled an insect from the grass.

4. Rewrite sentence D to have a:

a. compound subject:

_____

b. compound predicate:

_____

c. compound direct object:

_____

Practice working with compound elements in the exercises in your workbook, *Exercises in English*.

Name _____   Date _____

Try It: Sentence Diagramming

Sentence Diagramming Steps

1. **Verb?**
   Write the verb on the main diagram line.

2. **Subject?**
   Write the subject in front of the verb on the main diagram line. Draw a short vertical line (that cuts through the main line) to separate the subject and the verb.

3. **Direct object or subject complement, if any?**
   Write the direct object or subject complement after the verb on the main diagram line. Draw a short vertical (for direct object) or slanted (for subject complement) line between them.

4. **Verb modifiers, if any?**
   Write the modifiers on slanted lines below the verb.

5. **Subject modifiers, if any?**
   Write the modifiers on slanted lines below the subject.

6. **Direct object or subject complement modifiers, if any?**
   Write the modifiers on slanted lines below the direct object or subject complement.

7. **Modifiers of modifiers, if any?**
   Write the modifiers below the words they modify on L-shaped lines.

8. **Prepositional phrases?**
   Write the phrases below the words they modify, with the preposition on a slanted line and its object on a connected horizontal line.

Diagram the five sentences below, which are from Try It Yourself on page 158 of *Exercises in English*. Ask for help if you need it.

1. A severe storm completely ruined the beautiful garden near our garage.

2. Carol was the winner of the first prize.

3. Lewis and Clark bravely explored the mountains of the West.

4. The helpful children washed and polished the old silverware.

5. The creaking old house was extremely scary.

Name _____   Date _____

Get Ready

Natural and Inverted Sentence Order

It's a windy summer day, and you're sitting under a tree writing a letter to a friend, trying to describe the whisper of the wind in the branches overhead. Which of the following sentences would you use? (Both sentences have the same meaning, and both are perfectly correct.)

1. The leaves rustle gently in the breeze.
2. Gently rustle the leaves in the breeze.

Most people would probably choose Sentence 1, which is in *natural order*. When a sentence has natural order, the subject comes before, or precedes, the verb. In Sentence 1, the subject *leaves* comes before the verb *rustle*.

Sentence 2, on the other hand, is in *inverted order*. *Inverted* can mean *reversed*. In inverted sentence order, the verb or part of the verb comes before the subject—the reverse of natural order. In Sentence 2, the verb *rustle* precedes the subject *leaves*.

Here are some more examples of sentence order. The first sentence of each pair is in natural order, and the second is in inverted order.

A very dirty Bobby crawled out from under the porch.
Out from under the porch crawled a very dirty Bobby.

The canoe slapped against the dock.
Against the dock slapped the canoe.

This train travels between Memphis and Nashville.
Between Memphis and Nashville travels this train.

Inverted Sentence Order in Questions

Inverted order is common in questions, or *interrogative sentences*. Questions usually include divided verb phrases, with the auxiliary verb preceding the subject and the main verb coming after it.

Here is a question with inverted order—*rustle*'s auxiliary verb *do* comes before the subject *leaves.*

Do the leaves rustle gently in the breeze?

Add Some Style

In everyday written and spoken English, most sentences are in natural order. Inverted order is pretty rare.

However, in poetic language, inverted order appears more frequently, as you can see in the underlined sections of these poem excerpts.

Behind him <u>lay the gray Azores</u>
   Behind the Gates of Hercules;
Before him not the ghost of shores,
   Before him only shoreless seas
     …
They sailed. They sailed. Then <u>spoke the mate</u>:
   "This mad sea shows his teeth tonight.
He curls his lip, he lies in wait,
   With lifted teeth, as if to bite!"
           from *Columbus,* by Joaquin Miller

Here at our sea-washed, sunset gates <u>shall stand</u>
<u>A mighty woman</u> with a torch, whose flame
Is the imprisoned lightning, and her name
Mother of Exiles. From her beacon-hand <u>glows</u>
<u>world-wide welcome</u>; her mild eyes command
The air-bridged harbor that twin cities frame.
from *The New Colossus,* by Emma Lazarus

Though you will rely most on natural order in your writing and speech, you can add variety and style by occasionally creating a sentence in inverted order. Give it a try. May your results be pleasing!

Name _____   Date _____

Try It

Are these sentences in natural (N) or inverted (I) order? Label them on the lines.

1. _____ In her ear buzzed a mosquito.

2. _____ He needs to use the sewing machine today.

3. _____ Can you see Mt. Washington from here?

4. _____ When will the bluegrass concert begin?

5. _____ Long ago lived a queen in a castle.

6. _____ Jimmy is mowing the lawn because Dad broke his leg.

Write two sentences using inverted order.

7. _____

8. _____

Name _____   Date _____

Get Ready

Four Kinds of Sentences

Match the four kinds of sentences with their descriptions. Each numbered sentence type will have two lettered descriptions.

1. _____ declarative sentence

2. _____ interrogative sentence

3. _____ imperative sentence

4. _____ exclamatory sentence

a. gives a command or makes a strong request
b. ends in a period
c. ends in an exclamation point
d. makes a statement
e. ends in a question mark
f. expresses strong emotion
g. ends in a period or an exclamation point
h. asks a question

Rewriting Sentences

Every day you have to decide what to wear. What you choose probably depends somewhat on what you are doing that day or your mood. Nobody looks or acts exactly the same every day—thank goodness!

Sentences can also keep their basic meanings but change to fit the situation. Let's look at a declarative sentence:

Tom does amazing snowboard tricks.

With a few changes in wording and punctuation, a declarative sentence can become:

- *an exclamatory sentence*:
  Wow, Tom can do amazing snowboard tricks!

- *an imperative sentence*:
  Tom, do some of your amazing snowboard tricks.

- *an interrogative sentence*:
  Can Tom really do amazing snowboard tricks?

Let's look at another one. Here's an imperative sentence:

Stay away from that dangerous construction site!

Again, with a few changes in wording and punctuation, you can rewrite an imperative sentence into:

- *an exclamatory sentence*:
  That construction site is dangerous!

- *an interrogative sentence*:
  Are you staying away from that dangerous construction site?

- *a declarative sentence*:
  We'll stay away from that dangerous construction site.

Name _____ Date _____

Get Ready

Who Am I?

Match the lettered names to their descriptions. Read and think carefully!

Hints: Two lettered names will be used more than once.

Four lettered names will not be used at all.

1. ____ I am an adjective that may mean "reversed."

2. ____ I am two or more nouns or pronouns that receive a verb's action.

3. ____ I am the most common kind of sentence order in English.

4. ____ I ask a question.

5. ____ I always end in an exclamation point.

6. ____ In my kind of sentence order, the verb or part of the verb precedes the subject.

7. ____ I am an adjective that means "made from a mixture of different things."

8. ____ I am who or what the sentence is about, with all my modifiers.

9. ____ I give a command or make a strong request.

10. ____ I tell what the subject is or does, without any modifiers, objects, or complements.

11. ____ Help! I'm incomplete! I am missing a subject, or a predicate, or both!

12. ____ I am two or more verbs that show what one subject is or does.

13. ____ My kind of sentence order is more common in poetic language than in everyday language.

14. ____ If you find me, please rewrite me into a complete sentence.

a. compound
b. declarative sentence
c. natural
d. interrogative sentence
e. compound direct object
f. inverted
g. compound subject
h. imperative sentence
i. simple subject
j. exclamatory sentence
k. complete predicate
l. fragment
m. simple predicate
n. compound predicate
o. complete subject

Name _____   Date _____

Try It

Today you're going to review what you've learned in Units 7, 8, and 9.

Part 1:
Complete each sentence with the simple past or the past participle of the verb.

Example:
   catch   Daniel had ___caught___ five fish at the end of the day.

1. **ask**   We _____ our dance instructor to show us the new step one more time.

2. **write**   Mark had _____ a letter to the editor of the newspaper.

3. **pretend** The boy _____ to be asleep when his dog jumped on the bed.

Part 2:
Circle the correct form of the verb to complete each sentence.

4. Has Antonio (took, taken) the video back to the store yet?

5. She was (chose, chosen) to be the speaker at the meeting.

6. I (gone, went) to the doctor and the dentist last Thursday.

7. Cody (seen, saw) a wild turkey in the woods.

Part 3:
Complete each sentence with the verb requested in parentheses.

8. They _____ for the store to open.
(past progressive tense, *wait*)

9. She _____ her twin boys along the sidewalk in a large stroller.
(simple past tense, *push*)

10. Does Michael think the team _____ the game today?
(simple future tense, *win*)

11. Mrs. Jenkins _____ fresh bread every Monday morning.
(simple present tense, *bake*)

12. I _____ a surprise for my piano teacher.
(present progressive tense, *plan*)

Part 4:
Write sentences using each verb as requested.

13. (*opened* as a transitive verb)

_____

14. (*smiled* as an intransitive verb)

_____

15. (*painted* as a transitive verb)

_____

Part 5:
Circle the correct word in parentheses.

16. Please (let, leave) your backpacks by the door.

17. Thank you for (letting, leaving) me borrow your calculator.

18. Will you please (teach, learn) me how to play the harmonica?

19. I hope I can (teach, learn) my lines for the play.

20. This is a (good, well) pot for planting our daisies.

21. Charlotte can speak French (good, well).

22. It is (real, very) cloudy outdoors today.

23. The lamp was filled with (real, very) seashells.

24. Jennifer (has, have) a collection of antique dolls.

25. A large flag (fly, flies) above the school.

Part 6:
Complete each sentence with the kind of adverb requested in parentheses.

26. The washing machine _____ rattles when the clothes are spinning. (adverb of time)

27. The line of people moved _____ when the man blew his whistle. (adverb of place)

28. Mr. Thompson spoke _____ to the boys who weeded his garden.
    (adverb of manner)

29. The children _____ ran into the house when it began to rain.
    (positive form of *quickly*)

30. Daniel makes friends _____ than his brother does.
    (comparative form of *easily*)

31. My kite flew _____ of all the kites in the park.
    (superlative form of *high*)

Part 7:
Circle the correct word to complete the sentence.

32. None of the children has _____ ridden a roller coaster.
    a. ever
    b. never

33. Wasn't there _____ left to eat after the party?
    a. anything
    b. nothing

34. I see _____ empty parking places near the theater.
    a. no
    b. any

35. Marsha has _____ spent the night at my house.
    a. ever
    b. never

Name _____ Date _____

Try It

Today you're going to review what you've learned in Units 10, 11, and 12.

Part 1:
Complete each sentence with a prepositional phrase.

Example: She fell <u>down the slippery hill</u>.

1. All of the horses ran _____.

2. Two small boats sailed _____.

3. Jessica tossed her jacket _____.

Part 2:
Circle the correct preposition to complete each sentence.

4. The members of the chorus were talking _____ themselves before the concert began.
   a. between
   b. among

5. Please don't fall _____ the pier when you go fishing!
   a. off
   b. off of

6. We have a new neighbor who just moved here _____ France.
   a. From
   b. off

7. I was stuck _____ two noisy people on the bus.
    a. between
    b. among

Part 3:
Underline the adverbial phrase in each sentence.
On the blank line, write the verb that the phrase modifies.

Example: We rested <u>under the tree</u>.   ____rested____

8.   Jerry jumped over the neighbor's fence.   _____

9.   The pigs hurried to the feeding trough.   _____

Part 4:
Underline the adjectival phrase in each sentence.
On the blank line, write the noun that the phrase modifies.

Example: The flowers <u>on my sweater</u> are embroidered.   ____flowers____

10. Mom's pies in the oven are almost done.   _____

11. The panda bears at the zoo are my favorite animals.   _____

Part 5:
Complete each sentence with a conjunction to connect the subjects.
Example: Pencils <u>and</u> pens are in the drawer.

12. A police officer _____ a fireman is scheduled to speak to our Safety Club tonight.

13. Bananas _____ peanut butter make a delicious sandwich.

Part 6:

Complete each sentence. Use a conjunction to connect the predicates.
Example: The man snored <u>and</u> twitched his feet.

14. My sister made a mess _____ did not clean it up.

15. Each morning Matthew showers _____ brushes his teeth.

Part 7:

Complete each sentence. Use a conjunction to connect the direct objects.
Example: I am buying a sandwich <u>and</u> a carton of milk in the cafeteria.

16. Mrs. Morris knits sweaters _____ mittens for her children every winter.

17. We will cook hamburgers _____ hot dogs on the grill this afternoon.

Part 8:

Write a conjunction on each line to connect the two sentences. Use *and, but*, or *or*.
Example: I like vanilla ice cream, <u>but</u> I like chocolate better.

18. This book is interesting, _____ the book I read last week was much better.

19. I like to canoe on the lake during the summer, _____ I enjoy ice skating
there during the winter.

20. I dropped my lunch box, _____ my food went flying everywhere!

Part 9:
Write an appropriate interjection on each line.

21. _____ Your new bicycle is great.

22. _____ We won our swim meet.

23. _____ The baby is asleep.

Part 10:
Read the sentences. Combine each pair of sentences into one sentence with a compound subject.

Example: My hands are shaking. My feet are shaking.

  My hands and feet are shaking. _____

24. Peanuts were in the basket. Pretzels were in the basket.

_____

_____

25. Lizards are found in a rain forest. Snakes are found in a rain forest.

_____

_____

26. Tomatoes were in the salad. Cucumbers were in the salad.

_____

_____

Part 11:

Read the sentences. Combine each pair of sentences into one sentence with a compound predicate.

Example: The seagull screeched. It flew away.

  The seagull screeched and flew away.

27. I wrote my poem. I printed it on my computer.

   _____

   _____

28. The conductor tapped his baton. He looked at the orchestra.

   _____

   _____

29. Morgan has a snack. She takes a nap.

   _____

   _____

Part 12:

Complete each sentence with a compound direct object.
Example: Do you want to drink <u>milk</u> or <u>juice</u>?

30. I put _____ and _____ in my suitcase.

31. The children painted _____ and _____ on the mural.

Part 13:
Read each sentence. Is it in natural or inverted order? Circle the correct answer.

32. Under the stairs is a small closet.
    a. natural
    b. inverted

33. You are playing my favorite song.
    a. natural
    b. inverted

34. Frost is covering the ground this morning.
    a. natural
    b. inverted

35. Near the corner is a bus stop.
    a. natural
    b. inverted